# A Finite Element Dynamics Primer

# A Finite Element Dynamics Primer

E(

D.

COPYRIGHT 1992

ISBN 1 874376 05 0

PUBLISHED BY
NAFEMS
BIRNIEHILL
EAST KILBRIDE
GLASGOW, G75 0QU

Printed in Great Britain by Bell and Bain Ltd, Glasgow

# CONTENTS

# PREFACE

This book is intended to address the problems that a practicing finite element analyst might encounter when carrying out a vibration analysis. It is not intended to be a text book on dynamics, of which there are many excellent examples suggested in the bibliography. The contents are more concerned with giving practical help and advice to an analyst, both before he starts the analysis and in isolating possible problems that might occur as the analysis is being conducted. This makes the layout of the text rather different from other books on dynamics. It can be considered to consist of two sections, the first being chapter 1 and the second section being the rest of the book. Chapter 1 consists of brief notes and comments in terms of guidelines for a dynamic analysis. This can be used to remind the analyst of possible pitfalls associated with any analysis. However, dynamics are more complicated than statics and there are many more variations of problem and solution types. All of these possible combinations means that it is impossible to give a complete list of guidelines and so the second section of the book, from chapter 2 onwards, expands the brief notes given in chapter 1. These are intended to explain to the analyst the underlying theory associated with the brief notes so that he can adapt and interpret the comments to suit his own special problem.

No mathematics is given in chapter 1 but some has to be given in the subsequent chapters to explain the problems under discussion. The mathematics is not complete and is intended to be sufficient for the purposes of explanation. More detailed development of the mathematics associated with a dynamic analysis can be found in dynamics text books. The contents of each chapter is orientated to the finite element analysis rather than development of vibration theory. As explained above, chapter 1 contains the general guidelines. One of the problems with carrying out any dynamic analysis is the wide variety of problem types and solution types and the plethora of possible solution methods that this can give rise to. Chapters 2 presents details of the solution methods and the types of problem that each is most suited to solving. Chapters 3 and 4 give modelling suggestions, chapter 3 being concerned with general dynamic modelling and chapter 4 with aspects more specific to the finite element method. Forms of problem reduction, associated with trying to minimise the cost of the analysis are discussed in chapter 5. Since dynamics are less well understood and more difficult to solve than statics there is often a parallel dynamic test program conducted where aspects of the dynamic problem are confirmed by experiment. Chapter 6 discusses some problems of matching test and theory. The basic parameters of a dynamic analysis, the structural stiffness and mass and the applied loadings are usually well defined. However, practical vibrations also have a degree of damping associated with them. The nature of this is imprecise and the assumptions and approximations are detailed in chapter 7. The considerations associated with controlling and understanding the output are presented in chapter 8. One important point to consider here is the shear volume of data that a dynamic analysis can generate. Chapter 9 presents some information of the rather specialised topics of random vibrations and seismic analysis.

The book is not intended to be read from cover to cover. It is anticipated that only sections, not even complete chapters, will be read, as required by the problem in hand. With this in mind, and with the form of the organisation of the text associated with discussing possible problems and providing hints and tips, there is a repetition of some information. An attempt has been made to minimise this but the attitude adopted was that it is better to repeat some comments and warnings if this prevents mistakes from being made, rather than having too many cross-references which might not be followed.

The general layout and the contents of this dynamics primer was defined by the NAFEMS dynamic working group. The members of this group have also provided invaluable comments and criticisms as the text progressed and I would like to express my great thanks and gratitude for all of their work. However, I must take responsibility for any faults or limitations of the final text.

Dennis Hitchings
September 1991

# ACKNOWLEDGEMENTS

I am especially indebted to the following members, both past and present, of the NAFEMS Dynamics Working Group for all their help and advice in preparing this primer.

Prof A Morris Chairman
Mr H Chan
Dr M Fox
Mr A Humpries
Dr J Maguire
Dr M Petyt
Dr C Stavrinidis
Dr P Spence
Dr P Ward

With special thanks to John Maguire and Costas Stavrinidis for contributing significant volumes of material that have been incorporated into the text.

# CHAPTER 1 - BASIC CONSIDERATIONS FOR A DYNAMIC ANALYSIS

## 1.1 Introduction

This manual is produced by the UK National Agency for Finite Element Methods and Standards (NAFEMS) as a compendium of good practice in relation to a dynamic analysis, together with background explanations as to why these recommendations are good practice. It is limited to all aspects of linear dynamic analysis, with special emphasis on the use of the finite element method in dynamics. It is intended to supplement and expand the dynamic content of the NAFEMS publication Guidelines to Finite Element Practice and the dynamics chapter of the NAFEMS Finite Element Primer. All of the contents of the Guidelines to Finite Element Practice are relevant to a dynamic analysis and are not repeated here. However, special attention is drawn to the planning, documenting and results recording sections and recommendations of the Guidelines. The correct organisation of the analysis is essential to achieving reliable results. The wide range of possible options associated with a dynamic analysis make a correct and complete record of all aspects of the analysis essential. Much of the theoretical description of the finite element method together with the mesh construction and checking chapters of the Finite Element Primer are also relevant and not repeated here.

## 1.2 Layout of the Dynamic Guidelines

This text is arranged so that the first chapter gives a brief introduction to the definition of the main terms (or jargon words) used in dynamics. There then follows a series of check lists and notes on the various aspects that should be considered when carrying out a dynamic analysis. Because only sections of these check lists are relevant to any given analysis there are many alternatives and combinations. There is much less practical experience available for defining good practice in a dynamic analysis than there is for statics so that the subsequent chapters provide a discussion on these check lists to allow the analyst to interpret them in any given situation. The references given in brackets within the check lists point to the sections in other chapters where the topic is discussed in more detail.

## 1.3  Definition  of  Main  Terms

A glossary of terms is included at the end of this text. The main terms encountered within a dynamic analysis are explained in more detail in this section. The terminology of dynamics is not well defined since the same basic equations occur in may branches of science and engineering. This has led to a proliferation of names for the same quantities. The names usually encountered within a dynamic analysis are defined here. Other names and definitions for the various terms are given in the glossary.

Any system must have certain characteristics before it will vibrate. It must have a stable position of equilibrium so that, if it is disturbed from this for any reason, it tries to regain this stable position. The restoring force trying to regain the equilibrium position is called the **stiffness force**. For structural vibrations the stiffness force is proportional to the **displacement** of the structure and the coefficient of proportionality is called the **stiffness** of the structure. The stiffness stores **potential energy** which, for structural systems, is usually the **strain energy** within the structure. For vibrations to occur the structure must also possess **inertia** so that when it reaches the position of equilibrium the **inertia force** causes it to overshoot. The inertia force is proportional to the **acceleration** of the structure and the constant of proportionality is the **mass**. The mass stores **kinetic energy** within the structure. Vibrations are a physical manifestation of the interchange between potential and kinetic energies. For a freely vibrating system with no damping the sum of the potential and kinetic energies remain constant. Energy can be added to the system if external forces are applied and removed from the system if damping is present. For systems that do not dissipate energy the maximum potential energy is equal to the maximum kinetic energy. The **velocity** of the structure is the rate of change of the displacement with time and the **acceleration** is the rate of change of velocity with time. When the potential energy is a maximum the displacement is a maximum. At this time the kinetic energy is zero and the velocity is also zero. When the kinetic energy is a maximum the potential energy is zero, the velocity is a maximum and the displacement is zero.

If the system contains some form of energy dissipation then it is said to be **damped.** If no external forces are applied to input energy into the system then the damping will cause the **amplitude** of the displacements to die away with time. All real systems contain some form of damping. A common idealisation used for damping is to assume that the **damping force** is proportional to the velocity of the structure. In this case the damping is said to be **viscous** and the constant of proportionality between the the damping force and the velocity is the **viscous damping** coefficient. However, for most structural systems the damping force is small compared to either the inertia or the stiffness forces. For this reason damping is often ignored when carrying out a dynamic analysis and, even when it is included, it is usually only modelled approximately. Within structural vibrations damping is only important under special conditions. The damping mechanisms within structures are many and varied and viscous damping usually only represents a simplified idealisation of real life. For viscous damping the **energy dissipated** for each cycle of vibration is proportional to the frequency of the vibration. It has been found experimentally that energy dissipated within a material is approximately independent of frequency so that a modified form of viscous damping called **material** or **hysteretic** damping is sometimes used to represent this. The material damping coefficient is the viscous damping coefficient divided by frequency. It is only defined for cyclic vibration and, as a consequence of this, it can also be represented as a **complex stiffness** or **complex Young's modulus**.

It is possible to have a situation where the stiffness force and the inertia force are exactly equal and opposite. In this case they cancel each other out no matter what their magnitude is. When the stiffness and inertia forces are self cancelling the system is said to be in **resonance.** The amplitude of vibration is then controlled by the level of damping within the structure. At resonance the external forces are balanced by the damping forces. The frequency at which resonance occurs, that is when the stiffness and the inertia forces cancel is called the **natural frequency** or the **resonant frequency** of the system. If an undamped system is disturbed from its equilibrium position and no external forces are applied then it will oscillate at this natural frequency. If an undamped system is excited at its natural frequency then the amplitude of oscillations will grow linearly with time so that the response can become very large. If damping is present then the amplitude of vibration will be limited by the damping so that they will not grow to infinity. It will, however, vibrate with a large amplitude and the lower the damping the higher the amplitude. Damping causes the the peak amplitude to occur at a slightly lower frequency so that the **damped resonant frequency** is slightly lower than the natural frequency but for typical values of structural damping this change is so small it can be neglected. If the system is excited at some frequency other than resonance then the amplitude of the response is largely controlled by the stiffness and inertia forces. In this case they do not cancel each other and so the damping force is generally not significant.

The **equation of motion** defining the dynamic behaviour of the structure is the equation of equilibrium between the inertia force, the damping force and the stiffness force together with the externally applied force. This is of the form:

inertia force + damping force + stiffness force = external force

or in algebraic form:

$$M\ddot{r} + C\dot{r} + Kr = R$$

The linear dynamic behaviour of almost any structure is controlled by an equation of this form. The various forces are defined in terms of the mass and stiffness of the structure, the damping for any energy dissipation mechanisms together with any external applied force. This is defined as an input parameter for the analysis. The dynamic response is found by solving the equation of motion. Before these can be solved the structural **boundary conditions** must be specified to define how the structure is supported. However, it is not necessary for the structure to be supported in any way. In many cases it is also necessary to define a set of **initial conditions** for the displacement and velocity at time zero in order to be able to solve the equations.

Any real structure has a **continuous distribution** of stiffness and mass and there can be many combinations of stiffness and inertia forces that cancel each other. The structure will have many resonant frequencies rather than one. For a continuous distribution of mass and stiffness the structure will have an infinite number of resonance frequencies. This does not mean that every frequency is a resonance since the amplitudes and directions of the stiffness and inertia forces have to be in the correct combination to cancel each other and this will only occur at discrete frequencies together with specific displaced shapes. These are the resonant frequencies of the structure. In practice the lowest resonant frequencies are usually well defined since they tend to be distinct enabling them be found without too much effort. The higher the resonant frequency the relatively closer it is likely to be to its neighbours and the more difficult it is to calculate (or measure) it accurately. For this reason the calculation of the dynamic response is usually limited to a frequency range defined by the the lowest resonant frequencies of vibration of the structure. High frequency response cannot usually be calculated precisely and some form of **statistical energy** measure of the response for bunches of modes is used. This is not very amenable to numerical modelling and is not discussed in this text.

It is not easy to define or solve all of the details associated with a continuous structure for anything other than structures with a very simple geometry. For this reason the solution of real structural dynamic problems introduces a further level of approximation by restricting the numerical model to a finite **number of degrees of freedom**. The number of degrees of freedom of a mathematical model of a structure is the number of possible independent movements of each mass particle used to define the structure. In most practical models this is the number of displacements used to define the system. There are various methods available to define the approximations, the most common being either the **finite element** or the **finite difference** methods. Although these use different strategies to construct the equations of motion once they have been found they produce very similar forms of equations and have identical characteristics when it comes to solving them. It is assumed in this text that the equations are formed using the finite element theory but the majority of the discussions apply equally well to a finite difference formulation. The system has as many equations as there are degrees of freedom and will usually have the same number of resonance frequencies. A **single degree of freedom** system has one equation of motion and one resonant frequency. A **multi degree of freedom** system has many degrees of freedom and many resonant frequencies. Since the resonant frequencies for a continuous system occur at discrete frequencies then the resonant frequencies of the idealised multi degree of freedom system can occur at the same frequencies. In practice, for finite element and most other forms of numerical models, this is true for the lowest resonant frequencies but the differences between continuous (that is real) systems and idealised multi degree of freedom systems increase with increasing resonant frequency. Generally the more degrees of freedom a model has then the larger the frequency range over which it represent 'real life'. In practice this is not generally significant since the majority of the structural response tends to be associated with the lower frequencies.

The **equations of motion** for a dynamic system are defined in terms of its **stiffness matrix**, its **mass matrix** the **applied force vector** and occasionally the **damping matrix.** In many instances the damping matrix is not defined explicitly because the damping is small and the mechanisms giving rise to the damping are ill defined. Within the equation of motion the inertia force is the mass matrix times the acceleration vector, the damping force is the damping matrix times the velocity vector and the stiffness force is the stiffness matrix times the displacement vector. There are as many of these forces as there are degrees of freedom, that is, a force of each type is associated with each degree of freedom. The stiffness matrix can be identical to that used for a static analysis. For both finite element and finite difference forms the stiffness matrix will always be **symmetric** provided that the forces and displacements are defined to act at the same points and in the same directions and they are numbered in the same way. If the structure has no supports the stiffness matrix will be singular since it can undergo **rigid body motions** and these do not induce any strain energy into the structure (there are no stiffness forces associated with rigid body motions). It will also be singular if the system contains any mechanisms either explicitly or because of the numerical approximations used in forming the stiffness matrix. If the stiffness matrix is singular then it will have some **zero frequency** resonances, the number of which will equal the total of the number of rigid body motions plus the number of mechanisms present. If the stiffness matrix is non-singular then the strain energy is always positive and in this case the stiffness matrix is **positive definite.**

The mass matrix is also symmetric and is usually non-singular. However, on occasions the mass matrix can be singular but this is always due to numerical approximations employed when it is formed. If a **kinematically equivalent mass** (or a **consistent mass**) formulation is used and the numerical integration employed to establish the mass matrix is not too crude then it is non-singular. For a kinematically equivalent mass matrix the kinetic energy of the structure is always positive and the mass matrix is also positive definite. The terms kinematically equivalent means that exactly the same assumptions regarding the **element shape functions** are used for both the mass and the stiffness matrix. In most circumstances it is possible to use a much cruder idealisation for the mass than for the stiffness and this often takes the form of lumping the mass at the nodal point. This **lumped mass** form leads to a diagonal mass matrix which allows the computations to be much more efficient. An extreme form of this is the **point mass** model where the mass associated with any rotational degrees of freedom is assumed to be zero and only the translational mass is included in the model.

If the stiffness matrix is called **K** and the mass matrix called **M** then the undamped equation of motion in matrix form is

$$\mathbf{M\ddot{r} + Kr = R}$$

where **r** is the displacement vector, **r̈** is the acceleration vector and is the second time derivative of **r**. The applied force vector is **R**. If damping is included then it is defined in terms of the damping matrix, **C** for viscous damping, and the equation of motion becomes

$$\mathbf{M\ddot{r} + C\dot{r} + Kr = R}$$

This gives a mathematical representation or a mathematical model of the real structure. It is an idealised and simplified model of the physical structure and, hopefully, the more complicated the mathematical model then the more closely it represents real life.

If no forces are applied then the **homogeneous undamped equation of motion** is

$$\mathbf{M\ddot{r} + Kr = 0}$$

This has a solution in the form of **simple harmonic motion** where the displacements are:

$$\mathbf{r} = \mathbf{r}_0 \sin\omega t \quad \text{and} \quad \mathbf{\ddot{r}} = -\omega^2 \mathbf{r}_0 \sin\omega t$$

Substituting these into the equation of motion gives:

$$\mathbf{Kr}_0 = \omega^2 \mathbf{Mr}_0$$

This can be recognised as an **eigenvalue problem**, where $\omega^2$ is the **eigenvalue** and $r_0$ is the **eigenvector**. $\omega$ is also the resonant frequency in radians per second so that the eigenvalue is the square of the resonant frequency. If $\omega$ is divided by $2\pi$ then it gives the frequency in cycles per second (Hz). If the system has n equations then there are n independent solutions to the equation and these are written in the form

$$\mathbf{K}\phi_i = \lambda_i \, \mathbf{M}\phi_i$$

where $\lambda_i = \omega_i^2$ is the i'th eigenvalue and $\phi_i$ the corresponding i'th eigenvector. The eigenvector is the shape that the structure must assume when it is vibrating with a frequency $\omega_i$ in order that all of the inertia and the stiffness forces cancel. This is a **normal mode of vibration** and $\phi_i$ is the **mode shape**. It is called a normal mode because it is undamped. The eigenvalue is sometimes called the **characteristic value** and the eigenvector the **characteristic vector**. The eigenvalues are also the roots of the polynomial obtained by expanding the determinant $\det(\mathbf{K}-\omega^2\mathbf{M})$. This polynomial is known as the **characteristic equation**. The terms **latent roots** and **latent vectors** are also used in place of eigenvalues and eigenvectors. There will be as many **modes of vibration** as there are degrees of freedom in the system.

Usually the mass and stiffness matrices are constant in which case the system is said to be **linear** and superposition can be used in the solution. There are many ways of solving the equations of motion of linear systems depending upon the characteristics of the structure and the forcing function. If the **transient** response is required, that is the detailed time history of the response is of interest, then it is best to solve the equations in the **time domain**. In the time domain the time history of the response is calculated. Alternatively, if the forcing function is **periodic** so that it keeps on repeating itself then the starting transients are usually of no interest. In this case the **steady state** response is required and it is best to solve the equations in the **frequency domain**. In the frequency domain the steady state response of the frequency of interest is found. It is always possible to switch between the time domain and the frequency domain by means of a **Fourier transform** and often this can be done with the simpler **Fourier series**. The response in either the time or frequency domains can be found for each mode of vibration and these are summed to give the total response. This gives various **modal solution** methods. Usually only a small number of the lowest modes are used for a modal solution giving rise to **modal** condensation or **modal truncation**. Other, non-modal, solution techniques are available. For the transient response the equations of motion can be integrated in time using some form of **step-by-step integration**. There are many variations of these methods some of which are **conditionally stable** in that they require the integration time step to be less than some value which is a function of the highest eigenvalue of the equations of motion. Other methods are **unconditionally stable** in that any time step length can be used. However, the results become progressively more inaccurate as the size of the time step is increased. These step-by-step integration methods are the only general solution techniques available for solving **non-linear** problems. The equations can be solved directly in the frequency domain by means of **dynamic stiffness** methods where the equations are solved at one frequency at a time. The number of equations used in a solution are often reduced by some form of condensation technique. These can be in the form of **static condensation** (often called **Guyan reduction**), **dynamic condensation** or one of various forms of **dynamic substructuring**. All condensation methods tend to be exact for a static analysis but are only ever approximate for dynamics.

The form of the forcing functions very often decides which solution technique is most appropriate. There is a main division into **deterministic** and **random** forcing. For deterministic forces the the exact force is known at any time. The classification of these forces then further divides into **transient forces** which vary with time in a non-regular manner and **periodic forces** which repeat themselves exactly again and again. The transient force usually passes through a maximum and then settles to a steady value in a relatively short time. The peak response is usually the aim of any transient calculation. For a periodic force any initial starting transients occur over such a relatively short period that they can usually be ignored and it is only the steady state part of the response that is of interest. For random forces the precise magnitude of the force is not known at any time. Instead it can only be described in terms of various statistical quantities such as its mean, mean square and variance. If these average quantities do not change with time then the force is said to be **stationary**. This is directly equivalent to a deterministic periodic force. If the mean quantities do vary with time then the force is said to be **non-stationary**. This is directly equivalent to the deterministic transient force. If the forcing function is random then the response is also random and only its statistical characteristics can be found.

## 1.4 The Major Differences Between Statics and Dynamics

There are many differences between a static and a dynamic analysis both in the problem specification and in the results interpretation. The extra terms that occur within dynamics introduces many more decisions that must be made by the analyst. It cannot be emphasised too strongly that a dynamic analysis is not just a simple extension of a static analysis even though it might only require a small number of additional data items to be specified as input data to a computer program in addition to those required for a static analysis. There is a much wider range of numerical techniques for dynamics and the results need not follow a form that would be common sense for a static analysis. Typically the maximum displacements do not occur at the same positions as they would for a static analysis. Other differences between a static and a dynamic analysis are listed in the following sub-sections.

### 1.4.1 The surrounding Medium

- The mass of the structure itself is likely to be exceeded by the non-structural mass. This can come from the payload carried by the structure and from heavy non-structural items such as engines and valves. It can also come from the environment such as snow and ice and plant growth. The effects of the non-structural mass must be included [3.8 and 4.9].

- The medium surrounding the structure can contribute to both the dynamic damping and the dynamic mass. This is especially the case for structures surrounded by a dense medium such as water [3.4].

- The surrounding medium can produce a significant loading on the structure, typically a blast load propagates through the surrounding media before it hits the structure.

### 1.4.2 Damping

- All real structures dissipate energy when they vibrate and this gives rise to damping of the structure. For most structural problems damping is low and the precise mechanisms are ill defined [7.8].

- Damping can be added to the structure in the form of dashpots or other dampers. It can also arise naturally as energy loss within the material of the structure. The material stress strain curve traces out a hysteresis loop as the load is cycled and the area enclosed by this loop is the material damping. Damping can also arise by energy being radiated into the surrounding media as sound or similar waves. Coulomb friction can occur on any components that rub together. There are many other forms of damping [7.3, 7.4, 7.5 and 7.6].

- Since the damping for most structural problems is low it is often idealised in a numerically convenient form so that the correct order of magnitude of damping is included but the distribution throughout the structure is not correct. The damping can be considered small if the damping force is more than an order of magnitude less than either the inertia force, the stiffness force or the applied force [7.9].

- The two common simple forms for damping are modal damping when it is included after the equations of each mode of vibration have been defined and proportional damping when the damping distribution is taken as a linear combination of the stiffness and mass distributions. Modal damping can be related to test values but is only relevant for modal solution forms. Proportional damping has no physical meaning but is computationally convenient. It can be used for any solution method [7.7].

- In some cases the damping is entirely artificial and used to improve the numerical stability of the solution process [7.6].

*1.4.3 Modelling Problems*

- The lowest modes of vibration generally involve mode shapes that minimise the strain energy and maximise the kinetic energy [4.3, 4.4].

- Minimising the strain energy requires that a detailed description of the distribution of stiffness throughout the structure is given. The stiffness matrix must be as accurate as possible [4.4].

- Maximising the kinetic energy is much easier to achieve than minimising the strain energy. A coarse description of the mass distribution with the masses lumped at the nodes is generally sufficient [4.4].

- More care must be taken with the mass description if the higher modes of vibration are required. This can sometimes be the case for wave propagation problems [3.10, 4.7].

- Since the lowest mode of vibration minimises the strain energy within the structure it will tend to emphasise any weak or flexible portions of the structure. This will certainly be the case if the equilibrium load path passes through the flexible portion [4.4, 4.5 and 6.4].

- Care must be taken over modelling flexible parts of the structure. Note that this is independent of the form or direction of any applied loading so that such weak parts might not be apparent from any static analysis [4.4, 4.5 and 6.4].

- Joints can be especially difficult to model in a dynamic analysis. They are often relatively flexible and ill defined. This is typically the case with a spot welded joint. They can, in some instances, be the major parameter in controlling the fundamental resonant frequencies of vibration. They have less effect on higher frequencies. If a structure is dynamically sensitive then care must be taken with joint details at all stages of the design [4.5].

- Supports can be difficult to model within a dynamic analysis. Supports that can be considered rigid for a static analysis are often quite flexible dynamically [6.4].


*1.4.4 Controlling the Problem Size*

- A dynamic analysis will always be more expensive than an equivalent sized static analysis. The model definition time is likely to be only slightly longer but the solution time and the results inspection time will always be considerably longer [2.15, 8.1, 8.2 and 8.12].

• A dynamic analysis will produce much more output than a static analysis. Each mode shape will have roughly the same volume of output as a single static load case. Each time step in a time domain solution can also have about the same output as a single load case. Within a dynamic analysis there might be thousands of time steps with the possibility of the volume of output data being orders of magnitude greater than for statics [8.2].

• The output can be reduced or controlled in various ways. The dynamic model can have fewer degrees of freedom than a static model. Alternatively a static model can be used but modal, static or dynamic condensation methods employed to reduce the size of the problem actually solved. The choice of which results are saved to investigate the response can be carefully chosen to minimise the volume of data without losing any significant information. The printed output can often be further reduced in size by careful sampling of where the response is presented, both with respect to where on the structure the response points are located and also where in time that they occur [8.8, 8.9, 8.10 and 8.12].

• A modal solution allows much more precision to be employed in controlling the cost of the analysis. In many cases only a small number of modes need be used in the response calculation and the individual modal responses can be used to indicate where the full response should be presented in detail [8.8].

*1.4.5 Response Differences Between a Static and a Dynamic Analysis*

• The maximum dynamic response is usually greater than the maximum static response for the same order of magnitude of loading [6.5 and 7.12].

• The effect of stress concentrations tend to be less important in a dynamic analysis. The meshes can generally be coarser for a dynamic analysis than for an equivalent static one [4.4 and 4.5].

• The increase in the maximum response comes from a dynamic magnification factor. If the structure is excited close to a resonance then the stiffness and inertia forces are tending to cancel each other and the response amplitude must be greater in order to maintain equilibrium [6.5].

• If the excitation is exactly at resonance then the amplitude of the response is controlled entirely by the damping within the structure [7.3, 7.4 and 7.7].

• For frequencies considerably below the first resonance or slowly varying time histories the response will be quasi-static and reasonable results can be obtained from a purely static analysis.


*1.4.6 Output Differences for a Static and a Dynamic Analysis*

• In some cases the aim of a dynamic analysis is to find the resonant frequencies and mode shapes rather than find a forced response. This form of output has no equivalent in a static analysis [2.8].

• In a dynamic response there is not a single response for a given loading. The response varies with time and frequency [2.5 and 2.6].

• In the time domain it is necessary to conduct a series of response calculations around the time of maximum response. The time of maximum displacement response will not coincide with the time of maximum velocity response and similarly the time of maximum acceleration response will not coincide with either. The maximum stress response will also tend to occur at a different time again [8.8].

• In the frequency domain, damping introduces phase differences in the response between points. This phase difference is generally defined by a complex number. The real part of the complex number response gives the amplitude of the in phase component and the imaginary part gives the amplitude of the out of phase component. The ratio of the real to imaginary parts can be used to find the phase angle of the response [2.5].

• In the frequency domain, the forcing function can also be defined by complex numbers if different components of the force are out of phase with each other [2.5].

• In the frequency domain the peak responses for displacement, velocity, acceleration and stress will not necessarily occur at the same phase in the response cycle and the response over all of the cycle must be found. If damping is present then different points within the structure need not reach their maximum at the same phase angle [7.11].

### 1.4.7 Range of Solution Choices

• The initial choice for a dynamic analysis is whether to perform the solution in the time or the frequency domains. As a general rule of thumb transient and non-stationary random inputs are solved in the time domain and periodic and stationary random inputs are solved in the frequency domain [2.3].

• The next choice is whether a modal or a non-modal solution is adopted [2.14].

• Modal solutions can be used for any linear dynamic problem. They have a relatively high initial overhead in that the eigenvalues and eigenvectors have to be found. Once these are known the response calculation is very quick and computationally cheap. Modal solutions are best for situations with many load cases or long time history loading or periodic loads with many frequencies contained in the signal [2.14].

• Step-by-step numerical integration of the equations of motion can be used for short duration transient response calculations. They are the only currently viable solution technique for solving non-linear dynamic problems of real structures. Conditionally stable methods with short time steps are best for non-linear and wave propagation problems. Unconditionally stable algorithms are best for linear problems (they are not generally unconditionally stable for non-linear problems) where the transient force duration is relatively short. The time step is then largely defined by either the rise and fall times of the force history or the lowest natural frequencies of the structure [2.13 and 2.14].

- Dynamic stiffness solution techniques (where the equations $(\mathbf{K}-\omega^2\mathbf{M})\mathbf{g}=\mathbf{G}$ are solved directly at the exciting frequency $\omega$) are best used for periodic forcing functions that are very nearly sinusoidal in form so that they can be defined by a small number of discrete frequency components. One major problem with the dynamic stiffness method is that it becomes numerically ill conditioned for lightly damped systems if the exciting frequency is close to any resonance [2.12 and 2.14].

- No matter what solution technique is adopted a knowledge of the approximate values of the lowest resonant frequencies is required in order to choose appropriate time or frequency steps. They also provide much valuable information at the results interpretation stage and for understanding the dynamic results [2.10 and 8.8].

### 1.4.8 Effects of the Mesh on the Results

- Generally a dynamic analysis can have a coarser mesh than a static analysis because the response tends to be controlled by the low frequency behaviour [3.10].

- If a shock type loading is applied to the structure then it will cause waves to propagate throughout the structure. If the exact nature of these waves is of interest then a regular mesh of equal size elements must be used [3.10 and 4.7].

## 1.5 Definition of the Analysis Objectives

The wide range of alternative solution forms and the need to control the volume of the generated output means that it is necessary for the analyst to define very carefully the purpose of the dynamic analysis before it is started. If this is not done at the outset then it is very likely that the consequences of the analysis will not be as useful as they might otherwise have been. The points to consider range from the definition of the dynamic problem to the form of output, including ensuring that the program chosen for the analysis is actually capable of carrying it out. It is even appropriate to decide if the finite element method is the most suitable form of solution process.

*1.5.1 Forms of Output*

- All of the forms of output presentation that are useful for a static analysis are equally useful for a dynamic analysis [8.2].

- The results should be available in a tabulated form. The possible volume of data means that the user should be able to tabulate summarised data rather than print everything. This should include the ability to tabulate any response quantity against time or frequency for a selected number of freedoms and elements. However, the reformatting required to do this for large volumes of data can be expensive itself. The times or frequencies of maximum response should also be tabulated, together with the positions on the structure where the maximum response occurs [8.1 and 8.2].

- The user should be able to produce graphs of response against time or frequency and distribution of the response along a line of nodes at any one time or frequency. In the frequency domain this should include the phase effects [8.2 and 8.9].

- Plots of deflected shapes are useful, especially plots of mode shapes for a dynamic analysis. These are even more useful if they can be animated to produce a moving picture showing how the structure is flexing [8.11].

- Contour plots of stresses are as necessary as they are in a static analysis. In addition contour plots of nodal lines for mode shapes can be very informative. If these are superimposed upon an outline deformed shape plot they are even more useful [8.11].

- All of these forms of output parallel directly what is available for static analysis. In addition special facilities are required for dynamics. The possibility of variations in the phase of the response means that information about this phasing should be available. This can be in terms of absolute amplitudes and phase angles or as real and imaginary components. Sorting on maximum values should allow for phase differences to be accounted for [8.2].

- The user should be able to produce mobility or impedance plots, with either direct values for loaded degrees of freedom or as cross values for other freedoms to allow comparison with measured quantities [6.5].

- Response locus plots (Nyquist plots) should be available [6.2].

- For all of these frequency response type plots the detail must be much finer around each resonance where the shape of the plot is changing rapidly. The choice of the fine resolution should be automatic [6.5].

- It would be desirable to produce animated plots of transient response but there is usually a limit upon the number of frames that can be stored in high speed memory for a dynamic animation. This currently limits the usefulness of animated plots to mode shapes and steady state responses. However, specialised processors are now available to animate almost any dynamic response and the increasing power of computers, especially using parallel processing, means that animation will become an increasingly important method of presenting dynamic results [8.11].

*1.5.2 Suitability of the Chosen Analysis Program*

- Before embarking upon an analysis the user must confirm that the required facilities are available within their working organisation. If these facilities have not been employed before by the user then they should be thoroughly tested before serious use [3.12].

- If a program only contains step-by-step integration schemes then they are not suitable for steady state response. In theory they can solve this problem type but the cost of doing this is generally prohibitive [2.14].

- The suitability of program facilities should be tested in pilot studies to confirm that they are usable. Problems that can occur here are condensation techniques where the cost of the condensation process increases more rapidly with degrees of freedom than does the cost of the full analysis [3.12 and 8.12].

- The user should confirm that the program not only allows various facilities to be combined but that such combinations still produce the correct answer. Such combinations might be the simultaneous use of mass lumping and constraint equations. Depending upon the actual implementation such a combination can produce wrong answers even though the individual facilities work correctly separately [3.12].

- The program should have the ability to find the first few lowest resonant frequencies even if a non-modal solution is being used. A knowledge of these is usually essential to deciding integration time steps, critical loading cases and important frequency ranges. The frequencies and mode shapes can also be used to explain the characteristics of the response. They are also used to determine areas of maximum displacement and stress response to aid in minimising the printed output [8.8].

- On some occasions the analyst should consider whether a full finite element analysis is appropriate. If the structure has a large, relatively rigid mass connected to a light flexible structure then it can probably be represented quite accurately as a single degree of freedom system [3.12].

## 1.6 Problem Types and Solution Methods

As a part of the problem formulation exercise the analyst should attempt to classify its characteristics in order to be able to choose suitable solution methods.

### 1.6.1 Natural Frequency Calculations

- There are many methods of finding the eigenvalues and eigenvectors of a set of equations. The finite element method produces a set of positive definite, or at worst positive semi definite, equations. They are also symmetric and are usually heavily banded. Often, in addition, only the lowest modes of vibration are required, typically much less than 10% of the total number of the total number of possible modes [2.10, 2.11, 3.10 and 4.4].

• The lowest frequency can be found by a power method which establishes a simple iterative scheme to find the eigenvalue and vector. These power methods tend to be unreliable for more than the lowest eigenvalue since they are prone to rounding error [2.10].

• The classical eigenvalue extraction schemes use some form of similarity transformation. These techniques are usually very accurate and reliable but they are only really suitable for problems with a small number of equations since the intermediate matrices they generate are fully populated [2.10].

• Sparse matrix techniques are the most useful form for typical finite element equations. These are designed to utilise the banded nature of the equations and only calculate the lowest natural frequencies. They can also be prone to occasionally missing one or more modes of vibration over the selected range. The most common methods are subspace iteration, simultaneous vector iteration (very similar to subspace and the two methods can be considered identical by the user) and the Lanczos method [2.10].

• The most accurate method for calculating eigenvalues are based upon Sturm sequence method. This only requires that the signs of numbers to be found, not the numbers themselves and are thus numerically very stable. They also allow individual frequencies to be found without having to find all of those below. However, they are also expensive to use and they do not calculate the corresponding eigenvectors. They are rarely employed to find all of the eigenvalues but they are used extensively to check if any eigenvalues are missing from those calculated using a sparse matrix method [2.10 and 8.6].

*1.6.2 Numerical Integration Methods*

• A transient response is often calculated using some form of step-by-step numerical integration. There are two categories for these methods conditionally stable and unconditionally stable [2.13].

• The conditionally stable methods require that a short time step is used for the integration. They usually find the response at the end of the step in terms of the conditions at the start of the step and are thus called explicit integration methods. Alternatively there are unconditionally stable methods that, for linear problems at least, allow any length of time step to be used. These usually find the response at the end of the step in terms of the conditions at the end of the step and are thus called implicit integration methods [2.13].

• Conditionally stable methods require a time step to be chosen based upon the highest eigenvalue of the system. In practice this can be approximated by the Courant condition so that the time step is smaller than the shortest time it takes for a disturbance to travel between any two nodes on the mesh [2.13].

• Unconditionally stable methods can have any value for the time step but the accuracy of the solution decreases as the step length increases. The step length must be smaller than one tenth of the time period that the analyst wishes to represent accurately. It can be made smaller than this if the rise or fall times of the forcing function are short enough to warrant it [2.13].

• Numerical integration methods tend to decrease the resonant frequencies (elongate their periods) of a system when compared to the frequencies of the same system found from an eigenvalue analysis. They also tend to increase the apparent damping of the system. This is especially so for unconditionally stable methods. If the time step is less than one tenth of the period of a mode then that mode will be accurately represented in the solution both in terms of frequency and damping [2.13].

*1.6.3 Classification of Loadings*

• If the sole purpose of the dynamic analysis is to find the resonant frequencies and/or mode shapes of the structure then the effects of loading need not be considered [2.8].

• If the purpose of the dynamic calculation is to find a forced response then the form of the forcing function tends to control the choice of solution method [2.3].

• Loadings can be deterministic time histories, deterministic frequency content, stationary random and non-stationary random [2.3].

• If the structure is linear and there are more than two load cases or one load case that has a long time history (more than fifty cycles of the fundamental frequency) or many frequency components (more than twenty) then it is best to conduct a modal analysis. Once the modes have been found then any form of forcing function can be solved. In practice the solution form must have been coded into the program, that is the choice of solution method is often controlled by what is available within the program [2.4 and 2.14].

• Deterministic transient response can be found using modal solutions or direct time integration methods. Care must be taken in the choice of time step. If the problem is non-linear then a step-by-step integration scheme (usually a conditionally stable one) must be used unless some form of equivalent linearisation is formulated [2.4 and 2.13].

• Deterministic frequency response can be found using modal or dynamic stiffness methods. Dynamic stiffness methods can be ill conditioned for frequencies close to a resonance [2.4 and 2.12].

• Stationary random responses can be found in the frequency domain using spectral density methods. The spectral density of the input defines the frequency content of the forcing function. This is used to find the spectral density of the response. The area under the spectral density curve gives the mean square value of the response. Care must be taken to calculate the response at a sufficient number of points around each resonance since this area defines most of the mean square response [9.6 and 9.7].

• General methods for calculating non-stationary random response are not well developed. Two approaches are currently used. One is to calculate the response of the system to a series of time histories of the non-stationary loading events. The maximum response to these is then enveloped and taken as the maximum structural response. Alternatively the series of loading time histories are used to generate a general response spectrum for the event. This is achieved by constructing a smoothed envelope around the complete set of loading response spectrums. This is then used to find the response.

The second approach is computationally more efficient but it suffers from the fact that phase information in the signals is discarded and the solution is only approximate. This leads to problems in interpreting the results [9.].

## 1.7 The Resolution of Modelling Problems

One of the main difficulties that the analyst has to face regards the choice of mesh for a dynamic analysis. A dynamic analysis is more expensive than a static analysis and an inappropriate mesh will either increase the cost greatly or give erroneous results.

### 1.7.1 Types of Mesh for Frequency Analysis

• Areas of low stiffness must be accurately modelled [4.4].

• Large masses must be correctly positioned in the model [4.4 and 4.9].

• Uniform distributions of mass and stiffness require a uniform mesh [4.4 and 4.5].

• If only the first few resonance frequencies and mode shapes are required then a relatively coarse mesh can be used [4.3 and 4.4].

### 1.7.2 Types of Mesh for a Dynamic Stress analysis

• The mesh must be comparable to that for a static analysis. If only resonance frequencies or displacements are required then a coarser mesh can be used [4.4 and 4.5].

• The stresses are best recovered by calculating the accelerations at any time using the condensed dynamic model. These are then applied as static inertia loads to the complete uncondensed model to give a snapshot of the state of stress at that time [8.13].

- Recovering the stress directly from the condensed dynamic model will tend to under estimate the peak stress values. A high stress concentration is likely to have a relatively greater error than more gently varying stresses. This is true whether the condensation has been achieved by only using the first few modes or by means of a Guyan reduction [4.3, 5.4, 5.5, 5.7 and 8.13].

*1.7.3 Types of Mesh for a Transient Analysis*

- If the rise and fall times of the input signal are comparable to the time period of the lowest modes of vibration then the same mesh that is suitable for a frequency analysis can be used to find the displacement response. If stresses are required a mesh suitable for a static stress analysis is required [3.10, 4.4 and 4.7].

- If a wave propagation problem is being investigated or if the rise and fall times of the input signal are much shorter than the time periods of the lowest modes (a shock input) then a uniform mesh of square elements should be used [4.7].

- For quantitative rather than qualitative calculations a uniform mesh that is sufficiently fine for a static stress analysis must be used. If only a qualitative exploratory calculation is being conducted then a much coarser mesh can be used [4.3 and 4.4].

## 1.8 Primary and Secondary Components

All real systems are complicated with many interconnections and associated components. For a static analysis any secondary structures can usually be swept away and not considered in the analysis. This is not the case for dynamics. Any secondary component is important, no matter what its size, if it has resonant frequencies comparable to those of the main component.

*1.8.1 Definition of the Primary and Secondary Components*

- The primary component is the one of interest to the analyst [3.3].

- The secondary components are anything else that connects to the primary component. This can be other structures, attached components, the ground or the environment surrounding the structure [3.3].

*1.8.2 Inclusion of Secondary Components*

- To investigate what should be included in the analysis in addition to the primary component a series of associated analyses are required [3.3].

- A simple model for a secondary component is set up. Any natural support conditions are included in the model but the freedoms that connect to the primary component are fixed. The natural frequencies are found and compared to those of the primary structure [3.3].

- If the frequencies of the primary and secondary components are within a factor of two of each other then both the mass and stiffness of the secondary component must be included in the primary component model. The secondary component should be included even if its mass is two or three orders of magnitude less than that of the primary. The closer the fundamental frequencies of the primary and secondary components then the more important it is to include a dynamic model of the secondary component [3.3].

- If the frequency of the secondary component is more than twice that of the primary component then its mass is added to the primary component and its stiffness is ignored. The secondary component can be ignored if its mass is small compared to the primary [3.3].

- If the frequency of the secondary component is less than one half that of the primary component then its stiffness is added to the primary component and the mass ignored. The other end of the secondary stiffness is grounded irrespective of the actual support conditions on the secondary structure. The secondary component can be ignored if its stiffness is small compared to the primary [3.3].

## 1.9 Boundary Conditions and the Environment

Very few structures are totally isolated. They are either supported on the ground or are surrounded by a supporting medium. The effects of these on the dynamic response must be considered at the modelling stage.

### 1.9.1 Supports

• Supports that can be considered as rigid for a static analysis can be flexible for a dynamic analysis. This can be especially true when comparing theoretical and experimental results [3.6 and 6.4].

• Supports and joints that can open and close, that is the contact problem, are non-linear [3.5].

• Supports and joints are difficult to model. It is sometimes necessary to run two models, one with the supports or joints modelled as being stiff and the other with them modelled as being flexible. This will give the range of possible frequencies and responses [3.5].

### 1.9.2 Support and Joint Damping

• A relatively solid support will still vibrate to some extent and even though the displacements are so small the velocities will still cause energy to be transmitted from the structure into the support. This gives rise to support damping. The apparent damping of the support is proportional to the product of the density of the support material and the speed of sound in the material. It has all of the characteristics of viscous damping [7.8].

• Joints introduce damping. This can be in the form of Coulomb (sliding) friction or fluid pumping by normal movement of the joints. These are non-linear and are usually idealised as equivalent linear damping or as modal or proportional damping [7.5].

*1.9.3 The Environment*

• The fluid surrounding the structure will respond dynamically with the structure. Pressure (sound) waves can be transmitted from the structure [3.4, 7.3, 7.8 and 7.10].

• At low frequencies the loading on the structure can be represented as an added mass [3.4].

• At high frequencies the loading on the structure can be represented as added damping [3.4].

• The full solution for a fluid which extends to infinity requires a coupling between the finite element model of the structure and a boundary element model of the fluid. Such a facility is not generally available in current programs although some systems are becoming available that allow the structure to be modelled using finite elements, the fluid using a boundary integral (boundary element) formulation and then coupling these together [3.4, 7.8 and 7.10].

• If the fluid surrounding the structure is itself bounded then standing waves can be set up between the structure and these boundaries. If the frequency of a standing wave is close to that of a structural resonance then a coupled fluid structure interaction problem must be solved. For contained fluids this can be in the form of a finite element solution [3.4].

• If the structure contains a fluid then the possibility of fluid structure dynamic interaction must be investigated. Low frequency interaction can occur as sloshing of the fluid. Higher frequency interaction can occur as acoustic waves in the fluid [3.4 and 7.8].

• If the fluid moves past the structure then the possible forms of interaction are much more complex. It can give rise to loading on the structure, damping, vortex shedding and lifting forces. The coupling is usually non-linear [7.2].

• The drag from the moving fluid can cause the structure to adopt a different equilibrium position. As the structure vibrates the drag force will cause damping of the structural vibrations. The drag damping is a function of the relative velocity between the structure and the fluid [3.4].

• If the body is bluff vortex shedding can occur. If the frequency of vortex shedding is close to a resonant frequency then large amplitude oscillations can occur as the structure absorbs energy from the moving fluid [3.4].

• If the body can generate lift then at low velocities the fluid will damp the structural vibrations. As the flow velocity increases this damping will decrease until it becomes zero. Above this velocity the damping is negative and the fluid is putting energy into the structure. Such a phenomena is called flutter and the speed at which it occurs is the flutter speed. Large amplitude oscillations can result if flutter occurs and it should always be avoided [7.10].

## 1.10 Rotating and Pre-Stressed Structures

If a structure has a mean level of stress (that is there is a membrane component of stress from the static loading) then this can affect the dynamic behaviour by altering its effective stiffness. This can occur either from applied loads or, more commonly, within rotating machinery from centrifugal forces. Typically the stiffness of a gas turbine blade can be dominated by its centrifugal stiffening with the elastic stiffness being negligible.

### 1.10.1 Pre-Stress Effects

• If the structure carries a mean static stress then any deflection will cause a re-orientation of the direction of the stresses and new internal forces are required to maintain equilibrium. This gives a a stress stiffness effect in addition to the elastic stiffness [3.6].

• The stress stiffening will be positive if the stress is in tension. This will increase the natural frequencies.

- The stress stiffening will be negative if the stress is in compression. This will decrease the natural frequencies. If the compression is high enough the stress stiffness can cancel the elastic stiffness and the lowest natural frequency will be zero. The load at which this happens is the buckling load [3.6].

- The importance of stress stiffening depends upon its magnitude relative to the elastic stiffness. The higher the mean stress the more important the effect [3.6].

*1.10.2 Rotating Machinery*

- The centrifugal forces in a rotating component will cause a stress stiffening. This effect alone would cause the effective stiffness of the structure to increase [3.6].

- The centrifugal forces are not the only forces present in a rotating machine, Coriolis forces can also be present. Where possible the magnitude of these forces, in relation to the stiffness forces and other inertia forces, should be estimated to decide their relative importance in the problem [3.6].

- The Coriolis forces cause extra terms to appear in the equations of motion which are not normally present. They appear as gyroscopic forces. These terms multiply the velocities. However, they are not damping forces since the gyroscopic matrix is skew symmetric. The leading diagonal terms are zero and the off-diagonal terms are equal and opposite in the upper and lower triangular halves of the matrix [3.6].

- The skew symmetric form of the gyroscopic matrix never dissipates any energy but it does serve to transfer energy from one mode to another [3.6].

- This energy transfer can cause unstable oscillations to occur, typically the whirling of shafts is one example. The dynamic behaviour can be unstable and the displacement amplitude can grow to large values. This occurs over ranges of the shaft rotational speed The system is stable over other speed ranges.

• The form of the gyroscopic matrix is not usually found in finite element programs and requires special solution methods [3.6].

• Most finite element programs do not solve the dynamic behaviour of rotating machines correctly where the effects of both centrifugal and Coriolis forces are included. These effects become increasingly important as the rotational speed of the machine increases [3.6].

## 1.11 Record of Assumptions

Almost invariably a series of assumptions and approximations have to be made when carrying out a dynamic analysis. These should be recorded so that their correctness or otherwise can be verified as the analysis is conducted.

### 1.11.1 Stiffness and Mass Idealisations

• Record assumptions regarding the choice of element and element behaviour [4.6].

• Record any pilot studies conducted to verify the correctness of the stiffness and mass idealisations [3.12 and 8.12].

• Record assumptions made regarding structural and non-structural mass. What was included in the model for the non-structural mass [3.8 and 4.9].

• Within the finite element program calculate the total structural volume, the total structural mass, the position of the structure's centre of gravity. Verify these against non-finite element calculations [8.13].

### 1.11.2 Primary and Secondary Components

• Record what was taken as the primary component [3.3].

- Record how the secondary components were modelled [3.3].

- Record studies on the secondary components used to verify the validity of their idealisation [3.3].

- Record any part of the system that was not included in the dynamic model with reasons why it was not included [3.7].

### 1.11.3 Loading Idealisations

- Record the load cases considered in the analysis [2.2].

- Record load cases not considered in the analysis with justification as to why they were not considered [2.2 and 3.7].

- Record the actual solution technique used to solve the forced response. Give the number of modes used and/or the time step taken. Record reasons justifying these choices [2.3, 2.14 and 3.7].

- For linear systems superposition can be used. If it is used then record which were the computed results and which were the superposed results obtained by combinations of the basic load cases. Record also the details of how they were superposed including the superposition factors [2.2 and 3.7].

### 1.11.4 Results Recovery

- Record what results were recovered and the reasons why these results and not others were taken [8.7]

- Record the maximum values of the response quantities and the points and time/frequency at which they occurred [8.2, 8.8 and 8.9].

- Record how the stresses were recovered, either from the modal stresses or from a static solution using the instantaneous accelerations [8.13].

## 1.12 Capturing of all Resonant Frequencies

The finite element method tends to produce a large number of symmetric, heavily banded equations. There are as many eigenvalues as there are equations but only the lowest eigenvalues are physically meaningful. For problems other than those of shock loads or wave propagation most of the response occurs in the lower modes. For this reason special eigenvalue extraction schemes have been devised to find the lowest modes of large heavily banded sets of equations. One problem with such techniques is that they can miss some modes of vibration in the range of interest. Subspace (simultaneous vector) iteration and Lanczos methods are the current forms of sparse matrix methods.

### 1.12.1 Frequency Range

- Decide from the characteristics of the forcing function and what range of frequencies are likely to be of interest. This can be done by finding the response spectrum of the force time history [3.10].

- Use the Sturm sequence check to find the number of resonant frequencies in the range of interest. This is numerically very stable and will give the actual number of modes that are associated with the model below the specified value [2.10 and 8.6].

- If the number of frequencies in the range of interest is excessive check the model for errors. A typical mistake is to use the wrong units for the material density [3.2].

- If there is no error, check the model for possible local modes, typically in a detailed model there can be many local panel modes that do not affect the overall behaviour. If this is the case remodel treating the components with local modes as secondary components with either added mass or added stiffness to the primary component. These checks can be done by means of pilot studies on the parts of the structure that are likely to be relatively flexible [3.3 and 3.12].

- If there is still a large number of modes in the frequency range reconsider the validity of the whole analysis approach in the light of the analysis costs, man time resource available and the accuracy of any numerical method for modelling a wide span of frequencies [4.4 and 8.2].

- Compute the number of eigenvalues found from the Sturm sequence check and confirm that no modes have been missed [2.10 and 8.6].

- If a significant number of modes are missing check that the structure is responding in all directions. Some extraction techniques only find modes that are described by an initial starting set. If this is the case and it has failed to find all of the expected modes then change the starting set, usually by requesting more starting modes. In other cases it might miss multiple roots, especially if the structure has geometrical symmetries [4.8, 8.4 and 8.5].

- If only one or two modes are missing repeat the eigenvalue analysis asking for 10% (or 5 depending which is the larger) more modes. Often the missing modes will appear in this slightly larger set [2.10].

*1.12.2 Static Modes*

- Modes with frequencies higher than those of interest will behave as static modes over the frequency range [5.2].

- Some systems allow the high frequency modes to be included by equivalent static modes. This is done by recovering the exact static stiffness for a selected set of freedoms using the eigenmodes and the static modes. The static modes are chosen to achieve this [5.5 and 5.11].

- The static correction is not important for resonant response but can be significant for the correct calculation of the off-resonant behaviour. This is important if the results of the dynamic calculation are to be used in subsequent calculations [5.2].

## 1.13 Measurement Comparisons

One intermediate step in a complete structural design is to compare calculated resonant frequencies with measured ones. Such comparisons must be done with care if they are to be valid.

### 1.13.1 Nodes and Measurement Points

- The finite element model and the experiment should be designed together since the most meaningful results can be obtained if there are nodes in the finite element model that correspond exactly to the measuring points.

- The measurement points are sometimes taken on secondary components (often small protrusions or joints) and do not correspond exactly to the numerical model node points. The secondary components can vibrate independently giving different measurements from those calculated.

- If the mass of the measuring equipment or the force application is significant then the numerical model should be corrected to include this.

### 1.13.2 Supports and Joints

- Many comparison problems occur by assuming rigid supports in the analysis model when they will never be truly rigid in practice [6.4].

- If the measured frequencies are lower than the computed ones the effect of adding slight flexibility to rigid supports should be investigated in the numerical model [6.4].

- Similarly joints will never be exactly rigid and the effect of adding small amounts of flexibility into the joints can be investigated for comparison purposes [3.5].

### 1.13.3 Loadings

- It is usually impossible to simulate the actual loadings experimentally [6.2].

- The numerical model should be analysed for the loadings that are actually applied in the experiment [6.6].

## 1.14 Use of Symmetry

There are various forms of symmetry that are possible within structures. These include mirror symmetry about one or more planes, axial symmetry where the structure is formed by rotating it about a centre line and cyclic symmetry where the structure is not axisymmetric but it is repeated a series of times about the axis. A typical example of this is a turbine disc with blades mounted on it.

### 1.14.1 Advantages of Symmetry

- Use of symmetry reduces the number of equations and reduces the cost of the analysis [4.8 and 8.4].

- Structures with symmetry tend to have repeated roots. Repeated roots can present problems to some eigenvalue extraction techniques. Using symmetry tends to separate the repeated roots easing the computational difficulties [4.8, 8.4 and 8.5]

- If the structure has symmetries then the eigenvectors will also have the same symmetries so that no information is lost [4.8].

- Enforcing symmetry usually makes it easier to classify and understand the mode shapes. This is especially true with repeated roots [8.4].

- If the loading only has a subset of the possible structural symmetries then only the modes with the loading symmetries need be found [4.8 and 8.4].

### 1.14.2 Disadvantages of Symmetry

- Most systems allow the specification of symmetry boundary conditions to be automatic but only give the response in the portion of the structure modelled. Generally they do not recombine the results of the forced response to give the response at all points on the structure [8.4].

- If the program does not have an automatic recombination facility then the use of symmetry is only really practical when the load cases also exhibit the corresponding symmetries [8.4].

- If only the resonant frequencies and mode shapes are of interest then the loading need not be considered and advantage should be taken of any symmetries in the structure [4.8 and 8.4].

### 1.14.3 Mirror Symmetries

- Mirror symmetries are enforced by modelling one part of the structure and applying appropriate displacement boundary conditions. The complete structure can be obtained by combining this part with various reflections of itself [4.8].

- For a single mirror symmetry half of the modes will have a symmetric shape and the other half will have an antisymmetric shape. Two eigenvalue extraction runs must be conducted, one with symmetry boundary conditions and one with antisymmetry boundary conditions [4.8].

- The antisymmetry boundary conditions can be found by fixing the displacements that were free for symmetry and releasing those that were fixed on the plane of symmetry [4.8].

- Quarter symmetry requires four runs on one quarter of the structure. All combinations of symmetry and antisymmetry are used to define the four sets of boundary conditions on the two planes of symmetry [4.8].

- Eighth symmetry requires eight runs on one eighth of the structure. All combinations of symmetry and antisymmetry are used on the three planes of symmetry [4.8].

- The cost of an eigenvalue analysis increases as some power of the number of equations. It is always cheaper to run a series of small problems with various boundary condition rather than one large problem with the complete structure [2.10 and 4.8].

## 1.14.4 Axial Symmetry

- Axial symmetry requires special axisymmetric elements to be available in the finite element system [4.8].

- The displacements vary as harmonics of a Fourier series around the circumference of the nodal circle [4.8].

- Each harmonic can be solved for separately to give the resonant frequencies for that circumferential harmonic [4.8].

- The absolute minimum resonant frequency tends to occur between the second and the eighth circumferential harmonic [4.8].

- After the absolute minimum resonant frequency has been found the lowest frequency of each harmonic increases with harmonic number so that only those harmonics with frequencies in the range of interest need be computed [4.8].

- Each resonant frequency will occur twice, once for the sine component of the harmonic and once for the cosine component. Only the sine (or cosine) need be solved for within the eigenvalue extraction since the frequencies are identical and the mode shapes are rotated by ninety degrees around the circumference. Care must be taken in computing the forced response if the forcing function has both sine and cosine components [4.8].

### 1.14.5 Cyclic Symmetry

- Cyclic symmetry has very similar characteristics to axial symmetry [4.8].

- The conditions of cyclic symmetry are difficult to enforce manually and facilities for doing this must be available within the finite element program. It is not available in all programs [4.8].

- Cyclic symmetry will produce repeated roots for all cyclic harmonics except the first and possibly the last depending whether there is an even or an odd number of sectors [4.8].

- Cyclic symmetry should only be used by an analyst who knows what form of results to expect and how the results from one sector can be manipulated to give the results of the complete structure [4.8].

### 1.14.6 Other Symmetries

- Other forms of symmetry can occur but facilities that exploit these efficiently are rarely available within a system [4.8].

- Repeated symmetries, typically a plate reinforced by many identical closely spaced stiffeners [4.8].

• Dihedral symmetry, where a segment is repeated as with cyclic symmetry but each alternate segment is the reversed with respect to the preceding one. These can often be solved using cyclic symmetry where the two segments are analysed together [4.8].

## 1.15  Use and Value of Pilot Runs

It is always more difficult to predict the results of a dynamic analysis than it is to predict those for a static analysis of the same structure. The dynamic response is controlled by more parameters making prediction more difficult. Even a single degree of freedom system has a different response for an excitation above and below the resonant frequency so that if the natural frequency is not known then it is impossible to say what the response will be. In order to define a realistic model it is necessary to be able to estimate the general nature of the response. Before embarking upon a full dynamic analysis this general nature of the response can be found by the use of small pilot studies. Such pilot studies are also useful for defining the regions and the general levels of high response allowing the output of the full system to be selectively printed and displayed with a high level of confidence that nothing of significance is being missed.

### 1.15.1 Pilot Studies for Steady State Analysis

• The fundamental frequency of vibration can be found from a very simple model [3.3 and 3.12].

• A knowledge of the fundamental frequency allows the user to define what is dynamically important [3.3].

• The peak displacement will be associated with the maximum displacement in one of the first few modes [8.8 and 8.12].

• The order of magnitude of the peak response in both displacement and stress can be found from a simple model [8.12].

- The pilot model can be used for parametric studies to investigate the importance of variations in the geometry, boundary conditions and material properties [2.13, 3.12 and 8.8].

- The effect of joint stiffness variations can be studied more easily with simple pilot study models. The results of such investigations can then be used to assess their importance before the full model is built [3.5 and 3.12].

*1.15.2 Pilot Studies for Transient Analysis*

- The pilot study will give wave speeds [2.13].

- The reflection and refraction effects at material interfaces can be investigated. If no refraction occurs then the secondary material can be represented as either fixed or free boundaries on the primary, depending upon the phase of the reflected wave [2.13].

- Small sample portions of the structure can be used to define the required mesh density for propagation of the input impulse.

- A coarse mesh pilot study will give an indication of the response but is unlikely to give the correct response levels, especially if the response is non-linear [2.13 and 4.4].

*1.15.3 Definition of Primary and Secondary Components*

- Real structures are usually complicated [3.3].

- For a static analysis the primary load paths can be modelled and the other parts of the structure ignored [3.3 and 4.2].

- For a dynamic analysis the primary and secondary components can interact and the presence of the secondary component can affect the response of the primary [3.3].

- If the fundamental frequency of the secondary component with the connection freedoms fixed is within a factor of two of the important modes of the primary then a dynamic model of the secondary component should be added to that of the primary [3.3].

- If the fundamental frequency of the secondary is not close to important modes of the primary then a simple representation of the secondary component can be used [3.3].

- Simple pilot study models of the primary and secondary components are sufficient to define their resonant frequencies [3.3].

## 1.16  Finite Element Modelling

The finite element method is the most common way of establishing the equations of motion of a vibrating structure of all of the methods that are currently in use. The finite element method is only ever approximate and new approximations are introduced for a dynamic analysis. The user must take care when defining the analysis model to try to minimise the consequences of these approximations.

### 1.16.1 Guidance to Finite Element Modelling Problems

- Multi-point constraints are often used to constrain freedoms to act in a fixed way relative to each other [4.9].

- Such multi-point constrains can be very useful tools within a dynamic analysis [4.9].

- However, they can have undesirable consequences in a dynamic analysis. If multi-point constraints are used with a lumped mass model then the effective centre of gravity of the lumped mass with respect to the rest of the structure can be moved. The freedoms associated with the multi-point constraints should be located at the centroid of the lumped mass to avoid this [3.8 and 4.9].

• Multi-point constraints will always increase the band width of the equations. If many freedoms are tied together with multi-point constraints then the band width can be increased significantly [4.9].


*1.16.2 Kinematically Equivalent or Lumped Masses*

• The kinematically equivalent mass gives the representation of the mass distributed throughout the structure [4.4 and 4.6].

• The element shape functions are used to define the kinematically equivalent mass matrix [4.6].

• A kinematically equivalent mass matrix will have the same banding as the stiffness matrix [4.6].

• The kinematically equivalent mass matrix gives the most consistent representation of the mass of the structure [4.4 and 4.6].

• For the low frequency response the fine details of the mass distribution are not required and a lumped mass model can be used [4.3].

• In a lumped mass model the masses within the structure is treated as lumped, or concentrated, masses at the nodes [4.4].

• The lumped mass matrix is diagonal making it computationally attractive [2.13].

• Any lumped mass model must have the correct total mass for the structure and the correct position of the centre of gravity. The mass distribution should be representative of the actual masses [4.3 and 4.6].

• There is no unique way to lump the masses and a variety of methods are available [4.6].

- The mass associated with rotational degrees of freedom tend to be small compared to the translational masses and are often subject to further idealisation. For a modal analysis they are often set to zero. For a transient analysis the opposite is often done and they are scaled up to increase their magnitude. This is done to enable larger time steps to be taken in step-by-step integration methods [2.13 and 4.6].

- The approximations in the stiffness matrix tend to over estimate the natural frequencies and the approximations in the lumped masses tend to underestimate these so that their combined effects often cancel giving good estimates of the natural frequency. The associated mode shapes however, tend to have a cumulative error [4.4 and 4.6].

- For forcing functions that only excite the lowest frequencies of vibration then a lumped mass model is usually good. As the input frequencies get relatively higher then the kinematically equivalent mass representation gets better [3.10].

*1.16.3 Element Selection*

- Often it is convenient to use the same model for dynamics as was used for statics [4.1, 4.2 and 4.5].

- Care must be taken if this is done to ensure that the static model contains all of the information relevant to a dynamic analysis. This includes the correct distribution of the mass, the inclusion of dynamically important secondary components and the correct boundary conditions for a dynamic analysis [3.3, 3.8 and 4.6].

- Where a new model is being constructed for a dynamic analysis then simple beam and plate models are often adequate to obtain a good representation of the response. Solid and three dimensional models are only usually relevant where stress concentrations exist or where the loading is a sharp impact and a stress wave propagates in the structure [4.5 and 4.7].

- It is usually more cost effective to use higher order elements with a kinematically equivalent mass representation than a larger number of lower order elements [4.6].

*1.16.4 Numerical Problems in a Finite Element Analysis*

• Various numerical problems can occur with a dynamic finite element analysis [8.3, 8.5 and 8.6].

• Some eigenvalue extraction techniques suffer problems with extracting the zero eigenvalues of unsupported structures. If a shift technique is used to find these then a correct order of magnitude for the shift value must be given or either the zero eigenvalues still dominate or the non-zero eigenvalues become bunched relative to the shifted origin and are difficult to separate [2.10, 2.11 and 8.6].

• The choice of the correct time step is very important for most step-by-step methods. For conditionally stable methods the step has to be small enough to ensure that the solution stays stable but large enough to ensure that the response can be found with a reasonable number of time steps [2.13].

• For unconditionally stable step-by-step integration methods the time step must be small enough to ensure that the response is accurate up to the highest frequency of interest. For wave propagation problems too large a time step causes the wave to disperse [2.13].

• Step-by-step integration methods introduce artificial damping and period elongation into the computed response. These become more significant as the time step is increased in size [2.13 and 7.6].

• Most solution methods require that either the stiffness matrix or the mass matrix is non-singular. In theory the mass matrix should always be non-singular but in practice this is not always the case. The mass matrix can be made singular either by under integrating the element mass matrix or by assuming zero rotary inertias for mass lumping [2.10, 2.13 and 4.6].

*1.16.5 Mesh Density*

• The mesh chosen for a dynamic analysis should be appropriate to the problem under consideration [4.4 and 4.7].

• If only the displacement response or the first few natural frequencies are required then a coarse mesh can be used [4.4].

• If stresses are required then a finer mesh must be used [4.3 and 4.4].

• If dynamic stress concentrations are to be found then a mesh comparable to that used for the equivalent static analysis must be used [4.3 and 4.4].

• A fine mesh is required in regions of the structure that are flexible and allow relatively large deflections with low strain energy [4.4].

• Any large masses must be included accurately both with respect to their magnitude and their position within the structure [3.8, 4.3 and 4.9].

• If the mass and stiffness is uniformly distributed throughout the structure then a uniform mesh of elements should be used [4.4].

• If the purpose of the analysis is to investigate the propagation of waves then a uniform mesh must be used to avoid spurious reflections on the internal mesh boundaries [4.7].

• The element size is dictated by the dynamic wavelengths within the structure. For a modal analysis it is the wavelengths associated with the deformations of each mode and for a propagation analysis with the wavelength of the wave to be propagated [4.7].

*1.16.6 Accuracy Versus Cost*

• A dynamic solution is always more expensive than a static solution using the same model [2.15].

- The accuracy of the solution increases with increasing number of degrees of freedom [4.7].

- The cost of the analysis increases as some power of the number of degrees of freedom [2.15].

- It is necessary for the user to choose a mesh that is a compromise between cost and accuracy. This choice can be made easier by the use of initial pilot studies [3.12 and 8.12].

# CHAPTER 2 - DYNAMIC PROBLEM TYPES

## 2.1 Introduction

At the start of a dynamic analysis two fundamental questions should be asked. These are:

a.  What sort of system do I have here?
b.  What form of results are required from the analysis?

The answers to these two questions define the best way to solve the problem to obtain accurate answers at a reasonable computational cost. One of the major difficulties with a dynamic analysis is that there are many different forms of excitation and response and this gives rise a plethora of solution techniques. Although any one of these methods can probably solve all linear dynamic problems it will only be efficient and deliver results in an immediately useful form for a small subset of the problem types. Before starting any dynamic analysis the user must classify the system type and the form of the results that are required.

## 2.2 System Components

There are three components to a dynamic system:

### 2.2.1 The Input Forcing Function.

This can be zero, if only natural frequencies are required, or it can be non-zero. If it is non-zero then there are two main classes of forcing function. It can be deterministic, where all details of the force are known at all times or at all frequencies. Alternatively it can be random, where only the average and probable values of the force are known. The forces can be applied loads such as point forces or pressure distributions, as time varying displacements or accelerations or some initial non-zero displacements or velocities at time zero.

### 2.2.2 The System Type.

This can be either linear or non-linear. The non-linear system is not discussed in detail since the calculation of the response of a non-linear dynamic system is rather specialised and has to cover many possible forms of non-linearity. For a linear system the principle of superposition is valid. If a complete loading history is doubled then the complete response is also doubled. If the response of two separate loading histories are calculated independently then their combined response is the sum of the individual responses. The response can be found in terms of the behaviour in each mode and these then summed for the total response.

### 2.2.3 The Output or Response.

If no forces are applied then all that can be found are the resonant frequencies and modes shapes (the eigenvalues and eigenvectors). Each mode can be considered as a displaced shape and the modal stresses found but, it must be remembered that, these are only relative and not absolute stress values and they cannot even be compared in magnitude between modes. If a non-zero load is applied then the same type of responses as for a static analysis can be found at any time or frequency. This can be displacements, stresses or reaction forces and, additionally for a dynamic response, the velocities and accelerations. If the forcing function is random then the response is also random and can only be found in terms of average and probable values.

## 2.3  Range  of  Solution  Choices

There are many possible solution choices within a dynamic analysis. Most of these can be employed to solve any dynamic response problem but for a given analysis some are more

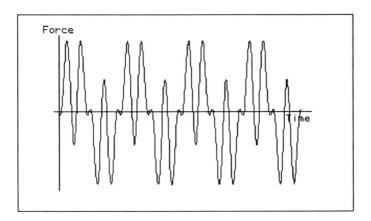

Fig 2.1 - Periodic Forcing Function

efficient than others. The type of solution technique that is best is largely determined by the characteristics of the forcing function. All forcing functions can be classified into one of four types:

### 2.3.1 Periodic Forcing Function.

The force amplitude repeats itself regularly many times. This is illustrated in figure 2.1. The simplest form of this is a sine or cosine wave, where the force is said to be harmonic. Figure 2.1 shows a more complicated form but this can be decomposed into a series of sine and cosine components by means of a Fourier series. For a linear system the response of each component in the Fourier series can be found separately and superposition used to add these together to give the total response. Because a periodic forcing function repeats itself many times any initial start up transient response is not significant and is usually ignored. Instead, the steady state response that the system settles down to is of interest. The most efficient solution methods for periodic forcing functions are those that calculate the steady state response directly. This is usually done in terms of the harmonic response in the frequency domain for each frequency in the Fourier series rather than in the time domain where the computation would have to continue long enough for the transient response to

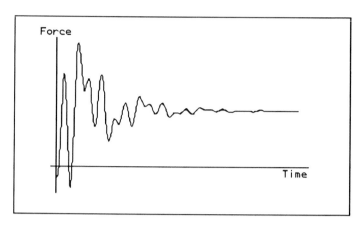

Fig 2.2 - Transient Forcing Function

have decayed away. This is typically fifty to one hundred cycles of oscillation for light damping.

### 2.3.2 Transient Forcing function.

In this case the force varies with time but it does not repeat itself continuously. An example of a transient forcing function is shown in figure 2.2. Typically the force rises from zero to a maximum or a series of maxima and minima as it oscillates until it settles down to a constant value. This steady value might or might not be zero. The force is described in terms of its time history and the time history of the response is also calculated. This is carried out in the time domain. For a transient response the peak values of displacements and stresses are normally of interest and these usually occur early in the response calculation, which is another reason for conducting the calculation in the time domain.

### 2.3.3 Stationary Random Forcing Function

In this case the force is not known precisely. If a sample of the force is taken and then a second nominally identical sample taken the two traces have the same characteristics but they are not exactly the same. In order to describe a random force then quantities such as its

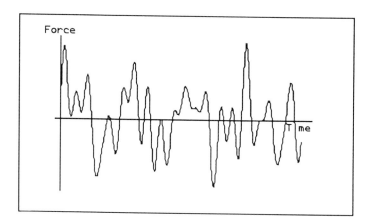

Fig 2.3 - Stationary Random Forcing Function

mean, mean square and autocorrelation (the mean of the product of the force at two different times) are used. These quantities are discussed in detail in chapter 9. If the statistical quantities are constant from sample to sample then the force is said to be stationary. Such a force time history is shown in figure 2.3. A stationary random force has many characteristics of the periodic deterministic forcing function and is also solved in the frequency domain. In this case the forcing function and the responses are described by their spectral densities (see chapter 9) which defines their frequency content. The solution methods that are used for finding the deterministic steady state periodic response are also used, with slight modifications, for calculating the stationary random response.

*2.3.4 Non-Stationary Random Forcing Function.*

Some random forces start from a low level, build up to a maximum and then die away again to a low level. Such a function is non-stationary random and is illustrated in figure 2.4. A typical forcing function of this type is a seismic (earthquake) event. Exact solution methods for non-stationary loadings are not well developed, largely because the data describing such events is not usually available in sufficient detail to derive the required statistical information. Instead approximate solution techniques have been developed. One

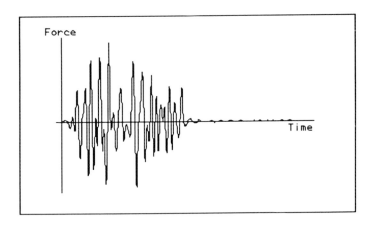

Fig 2.4 - Non-Stationary Random Forcing Function

is to analyse a set of such events using deterministic transient solution methods and to then average the results of these. Another, the response spectrum method, is a technique specially developed for approximate solutions of this type of problem. This is discussed in more detail in chapter 9.

## 2.4 Modal Solution Methods

A solution technique that is available for solving most linear dynamic problems involves finding the structures natural frequencies and mode shapes (eigenvalues and eigenvectors). If the structure has n degrees of freedom then it has n eigenvalues and n corresponding eigenvectors. In most cases only the first few of the eigenvectors are required. The methods for deciding the actual number for a given problem are discussed in chapter 3. The first p eigenvectors are found and combined together as the eigenvector matrix

$$\phi = [ \; \phi_1 \;\; \phi_2 \;\; \phi_3 \; ... \; \phi_p \; ]$$

Methods for finding the eigenvalues and eigenvectors are discussed in section 2.8 to 2.11. It is a property of these vectors that the product

$$\phi^t \, K \, \phi = k$$

makes $k$, the modal or generalised stiffness, diagonal. At the same time it also makes the modal mass matrix

$$\phi^t \, M \, \phi = m$$

diagonal. The eigenvector matrix is the only transformation that has the property to make both $k$ and $m$ diagonal. Very often the eigenvectors are normalised so that $m$ is the unit matrix in which case the modal stiffness matrix is the first p eigenvalues.

It is often assumed that the eigenvectors also make the damping matrix diagonal so that

$$\phi^t \, C \, \phi = c$$

Where $c$ is diagonal and $c_j$ is the damping coefficient of the j'th mode. The damping is discussed in more detail in chapter 7.

## 2.5 Modal Response in the Frequency Domain

If the structure is excited with a forcing function

$$R = Ge^{i\omega t} = (G_1 + i \, G_2)e^{i\omega t}$$

where $G_1$ is the amplitude of the sine (in phase) component of the force and $G_2$ the amplitude of the cosine (out of phase) component then it can be shown that the structure's steady state response is

$$
\begin{aligned}
r = g^{i\omega t} &= (g_1 + i \, g_2)e^{i\omega t} \\
&= \phi \, (k + i\omega c - \omega^2 m)^{-1} \, \phi^t \, Ge^{i\omega t} \\
&= H(\omega) \, Ge^{i\omega t}
\end{aligned}
$$

$H(\omega)$ is called the dynamic flexibility matrix at the frequency $\omega$.

$$H(\omega) = \phi \, (k+i\omega c-\omega^2 m)^{-1} \, \phi^t$$

It is a square (pxp) complex matrix. Since the matrix to be inverted when $H(\omega)$ is formed is diagonal then the calculation of $H(\omega)$ is very easy once the eigenvectors are known. The response $g_1$ is the in phase component of the response and $g_2$ the out of phase component.

## 2.6 Modal Response in the Time Domain

Again, once the eigenvectors are known the response can be found. If the force input is $R(t)$ at any time t then the displacement response is given at any time t by the convolution (Duhamel) integral

$$r(t) = \int_0^t W(t-\tau)R(\tau)d\tau$$

Where $W(t-\tau)$ is called the impulse response matrix. In terms of the eigenvalues and eigenvectors this is

$$W(t-\tau) = \phi E(t-\tau)\phi^t$$

Where $E(t-\tau)$ is a diagonal matrix with a typical term

$$E_{jj}(t-\tau) = \frac{e^{-\alpha_j(t-\tau)} \sin\beta_j(t-\tau)}{m_j\beta_j}$$

with $\alpha_j = \omega_j\zeta_j$ and $\beta_j = \omega_j(1 - \zeta_j^2)^{1/2}$ and $\zeta_j$ is the damping factor of the j'th mode.

It will be seen that the impulse response matrix is a (pxp) symmetric matrix The convolution integral can either be integrated numerically or, more accurately, the force history can be idealised as a series of line segments and the convolution integrated exactly.

## 2.7 Relationship Between Dynamic Flexibility and Impulse Response

The dynamic flexibility matrix is the Fourier transform of the impulse response matrix, which itself is the inverse Fourier transform of the dynamic flexibility matrix. Together they form a Fourier transform pair. Once one is known the other can be derived by a standard transformation. Similarly the response in the frequency domain is the Fourier transform of the response in the time domain.

## 2.8 The Eigenvalue Problem

The heart of many dynamic analysis solutions lies in the calculation of the eigenvalues and the eigenvectors of the system. These give a measure of which frequencies are dynamically important for the structure, allowing direct comparison with tests to be made. The eigenvectors provide a very convenient way to transform the equations to allow them to be solved. They can only be defined for linear problems but they are often computed as a first step for non-linear problems since they can be used to indicate under what circumstances the response is likely to be non-linear. The eigenvalues and associated eigenvectors arise naturally from consideration of the free vibration. There are eigenvalues and vectors associated with both the damped and the undamped free vibration problem. For most structural vibrations the damping is so low that it can be ignored initially and, as a consequence of this, it is mainly the undamped eigenvalue problem that is considered. The general damped eigenvalue problem and when it is appropriate to use this is discussed in chapter 7. For a freely vibrating linear structure with no damping the equation of motion is

$$\mathbf{M\ddot{r} + Kr = 0}$$

This can be assumed to have a simple harmonic motion form of solution

$$\mathbf{r = g}\sin(\omega t)$$

Substituting this into the equation of motion it can be shown that this satisfied provided that

$$\mathbf{(K - \lambda_i M)\phi_i = 0}$$

Where $\lambda_i = \omega_i^2$ and is the i'th eigenvalue. The corresponding resonant frequency is $\omega_i$.

Associated with the i'th eigenvalue is the i'th eigenvector, $\phi_i$. It is the purpose of solving the eigenvalue problem to find these for the structure under consideration. If the p lowest eigenvalues are computed then these can be combined into a single diagonal matrix

$$\lambda = \lceil \lambda_1 \ \lambda_2 \ \lambda_3 \ .......... \ \lambda_p \rfloor$$

and the corresponding eigenvectors can also be combined into a single matrix of the form

$$\phi = [ \ \phi_1 \ \phi_2 \ \phi_3 \ .......... \ \phi_p \ ]$$

In equations where $\lambda$ and $\phi$ appear then these can be taken to be the first p modes where p can lie anywhere between one and the number of equations. If p is less than the number of equations then they are called a truncated set of modes. The number of modes required for a dynamic analysis is discussed in chapter 3.

## 2.9 Properties of the Eigenvalues and Eigenvectors

The eigenvalues and eigenvectors are important because they allow the dynamic behaviour of the structure to be considered as the combined response of a series of single degree of freedom systems rather than the full complicated structure. This simplifies the user's considerations regarding the dynamic response and also allows efficient solution techniques to be derived. Physically the most important quantities are the eigenvalues since they define the critical frequencies for the structure. Mathematically the most important property is associated with the eigenvectors since it can be shown that these possess the ability of orthogonalising the mass and stiffness matrices. It is this property that allows the structure to be considered as a series of single degree of freedom systems.

If the structure has n degrees of freedom then in, in theory, it has n eigenvalues (it has n resonant frequencies) and n corresponding eigenvectors. If the structure is supported and has no mechanisms associated with it then both the strain energy and the kinetic energy are never negative at any instant of time. This has the consequence that the eigenvalues are always positive. If the structure can undergo rigid body motions or it contains one or more mechanisms then there can be zero strain energy associated with such displacements. This means that some of the eigenvalues are zero in this case. If the structure has $m_1$ independent rigid body motions and $m_2$ mechanisms then there will be a total of $m_1+m_2$ zero eigenvalues. If more zero eigenvalues than expected are computed then the possible causes are:

1) The structure is not supported correctly so that all of its rigid body motions are not suppressed.

2) The elements used have zero stiffness in some directions, typically a pin jointed rod or a membrane skin panel has no stiffness normal to its surface.

3) The element can be under integrated numerically so that it has possible modes of zero energy. Typically an eight node quadrilateral with in plane stiffness requires a 3x3 Gauss integration rule to be used when forming the stiffness matrix. In practice a 2x2 rule is sufficient if more than one element is being used and is often used in practice. However, if the eigenvalues for a single element using the 2x2 rule are computed then it is possible, depending upon the boundary conditions being used, to obtain a spurious zero eigenvalue.

The kinetic energy of the structure should always be positive irrespective of the boundary conditions so that there are no physical reasons for problems occurring with the mass matrix. Again, however, numerical and modelling problems can occur. If reduced integration is used then there will be spurious zero kinetic energy modes. In fact elements are more sensitive to this in their mass formulation than they are in the stiffness matrix. It is also possible to idealise the mass so that some displacements have zero kinetic energy. This happens with plate or beam elements that are idealised so that their rotational degrees of freedom have zero mass associated with them. If there are such zero mass modes then the corresponding eigenvalues are infinite. This is less of a problem than the zero stiffness zero eigenvalue modes but it does mean that the mass matrix is singular. If the eigenvalue extraction method being used relies upon being able to invert the mass matrix then this will cause numerical problems.

If the structure has geometrical symmetries then the same symmetries will appear in the eigenvectors. Considering a typical aeroplane that is symmetric about its centre line then half of the modes will be symmetric, the wing tips will be moving in the same direction, and the other half of the modes will be antisymmetric, when one tip moves up the other moves down. In such a case it is possible to construct all of the modes to be either symmetric or antisymmetric. Similar arguments apply if there are more symmetries within the structure and each symmetry can be considered separately. Taking advantage of geometrical symmetries can cut the cost of the analysis and it can also improve the quality of the results. Two modes, one symmetric and one antisymmetric, can have the same eigenvalue, in which case the equations are said to have repeated roots. The more symmetries a structure has the more chance there is of repeated roots. Some methods of finding eigenvalues have problems with repeated roots and using symmetry reduces these. Also, if there are repeated roots then any linear combination of the eigenvectors for these roots is also a valid eigenvector. This can cause problems with the interpretation of the mode shapes. Using symmetry keeps the roots separate and allows an easier recognition of the inherent mode shapes.

## 2.10 Methods for Calculating Eigenvalues and Eigenvectors

There are four basic categories for calculating eigenvalues and the associated vectors and within these four categories there is a multitude of possible methods.

### 2.10.1 Iterative Solution Methods

All eigenvalue problems of more than two degrees of freedom must be solved by iteration since it is finding the roots of an equation. The first and simplest eigenvalue extraction methods took the iterative form in its most direct implementation

$$\phi_r = \mathbf{M}^{-1}\mathbf{K}\phi_{r-1}$$

where $\phi_r$ is the r'th estimate of the eigenvector. This is normalised by dividing throughout by the term with the largest absolute value in $\phi_r$. This normalising value converges to the highest eigenvalue and $\phi_r$ converges to the corresponding eigenvector. The rate of convergence after n iterations is proportional to the n'th power of the ratio of the highest and second highest eigenvalue. For this reason it is called the power method. However, for structural dynamics it is the lowest eigenvalue that is of interest so that the power method is rewritten in the form

$$\phi_r = \mathbf{K}^{-1}\mathbf{M}\phi_{r-1}$$

which then converges to the reciprocal of the lowest eigenvalue and the corresponding eigenvector. This form is called the method of inverse iteration. Provide that the lowest eigenvalue is not a repeated root the power nature of the method gives rise to a very rapid convergence, usually within about five iterations. It is very good for finding buckling loads of structures where only the lowest eigenvalue is normally required. However, the high rate of convergence means that it is difficult to use the method to find any eigenvalue other than the lowest since any numerical rounding tends to cause the solution to home in on the lowest value. Two developments have been made to overcome this problem. One is the subspace iteration method discussed in section 2.10.3 and the other is inverse iteration with a shift. Say an eigenvalue has the known approximate value, g, then the shifted inverse iteration is

$$\phi_r = (\mathbf{K}\text{-}g\mathbf{M})^{-1}\mathbf{M}\phi_{r-1}$$

and this converges to the eigenvalue nearest to the guess g. One interesting point to note is that the inverse of $(\mathbf{K}\text{-}g\mathbf{M})$ becomes very ill-conditioned as g nears an eigenvalue. However, it can be shown that the associated numerical error in the solution is directly proportional to the required eigenvector so that for this problem the solution of a nearly singular set of equations is very well conditioned. If g is very close to an eigenvalue convergence is achieved in one iteration. Obviously inverse iteration with shifts is only really works if good estimates for the eigenvalues are available to enable good guesses to be made for g.

*2.10.2 Orthogonal and Similarity Transformation Methods*

The most reliable methods for finding eigenvalues make use of the orthogonality property of the eigenvectors to construct the transformation

$$Y_r^t \, Y_{r-1}^t \, Y_{r-2}^t \quad .... \quad Y_2^t \, Y_1^t \, (L^{-1}ML^{-t}) \, Y_1 \, Y_2 \, .... \, Y_{r-2} \, Y_{r-1} \, Y_r \; \text{-> a diagonal matrix}$$

subject to

$$Y_r^t \, Y_{r-1}^t \, Y_{r-2}^t \quad .... \quad Y_2^t \, Y_1^t Y_1 \, Y_2 \, .... \, Y_{r-2} \, Y_{r-1} \, Y_r = I$$

Where $L$ is the Cholesky factor of the stiffness matrix $K$ and $Y_r$ is the r'th transformation matrix. The diagonal matrix that the first product tends to is the diagonal matrix of eigenvalues and the product $Y_1 \, Y_2 \, .... \, Y_{r-2} \, Y_{r-1} \, Y_r$ gives the eigenvectors. There are various elegant versions of this technique but the ones most commonly used are the Jacobi method and the QR (or for symmetric matrices the variant called the LR) methods. In the Jacobi method $Y_r$ consist of sine and cosine terms to achieve the orthogonality of the second condition using the fact that $\sin^2\theta + \cos^2\theta = 1$. The angle $\theta$ is chosen to make each off diagonal term in the dynamic matrix $(L^{-1}ML^{-t})$ zero in turn. As one off diagonal term is made zero then the one that was previously zeroed becomes non-zero so that repeated sweeping of the matrix is required. The process usually converges after about 6 to 10 sweeps. The main difficulty with the Jacobi method is that it destroys the banding of the finite element equations since they become fully populated as a part of the solution process. This severely limits the size of problem that can be solved with this method.

The QR method also orthogonalises the dynamic matrix. It is the most stable method yet discovered for finding eigenvalues and eigenvectors and is applicable to solving any eigenvalue problem. It suffers from the same drawback as the Jacobi matrix in that it causes fully populated matrices to be formed as an intermediate part of the solution process. However, it is found that if the dynamic matrix is banded then alternate iterations cause the matrix to be fully populated at on step but to recover the original banding at the next. This has led to the development of the combination technique of first carrying out a Householder tri-diagonalisation followed by the QR eigen solution. The Householder transformation takes the dynamic matrix and transforms it to a triple diagonal matrix $T$ where the term $T_{ii}$, $T_{i-1,i}$ and $T_{i,i-1}$ are non-zero but all of the other terms in $T$ are zero. This process is well conditioned and can be carried out in a finite number of steps. Careful coding of the QR method for the tri-diagonal form then allows two sweeps of the iteration process to be conducted simultaneously so that the intermediate fully populated matrix is never formed, the matrix operated upon is always diagonal. The Householder process does require that an intermediate fully populated matrix is formed but this is only done once not on alternate iterations and so can be acceptable.

The main drawbacks with such eigenvalue extraction techniques such as the QR method is that they do cause intermediate fully populated matrices to be formed and that they always compute the full set of eigenvalues. The handling of the fully populated matrix is computationally expensive. For problems with over 500 to 1000 degrees of freedom backing storage must be used to handle the equations and this is time consuming. In addition there is no good way of storing the matrix on backing store. A product of the form $Y^t DY$ has to be formed and any backing storage scheme that is efficient for multiplying $DY$ is very inefficient for the resulting pre-multiplication by $Y^t$. The fact that all of the eigenvalues are computed but that only about the first 10% are required also makes such methods computationally unattractive for solving large problems.

*2.10.3 Sparse Matrix Methods*

To overcome the computational problems associated with the orthogonal transformation methods described in section 2.10.2 special sparse matrix techniques have been developed. These exploit the specific properties of the system of equations that arise within the finite element method namely:

a. The symmetry of the equations.
b. Their banded nature.
c. The fact that they are positive definite.
d. They only compute the first few lowest eigenvalues and eigenvectors.

There are two such techniques commonly used within systems, the subspace iteration method (which is essentially the same as the simultaneous vector iteration method) and the Lanczos method.

The subspace iteration method is basically the method of inverse iteration but working simultaneously with more than one eigenvector. If m eigenvalues and vectors are required than at least m vectors (the subspace) are used. At each step within the power method an (mxm) matrix is formed and the eigenvalues of this matrix are the current estimates of the first m eigenvalues of the system. These are usually found by either the QR or the Jacobi or some other orthogonalisation method since the (mxm) problem is small and can be held in core. Care has to be taken to ensure orthogonality at each step in the subspace iteration or the strong convergence of the first vector dominates. In practice it is found that the convergence of the m'th eigenvalue and eigenvector is very slow since it is continually being contaminated by the next vectors that are not included in the subspace. To overcome this if m vectors are required then m+p vectors are included in the subspace, where the extra p vectors (typically 5) are guard vectors and will not be computed accurately. However, their presence does cause a much higher rate of convergence for the m'th vector. Some systems add these guard vectors automatically, some require the user to specify how many are to be used and some systems require the user to request m+p vectors to be computed and he then discards the last p vectors. The system documentation should provide advice on what strategy the user should adopt in the choice of the number of guard vectors.

The Lanczos technique is rather akin to the Householder-QR method. Again the dynamic matrix is transformed into a tri-diagonal matrix and the QR method used to find the eigenvalues. However, in this case a special form of tri-diagonalisation is employed where the intermediate products of the transformation are never required and so the banded nature of the equations is always preserved. Further, only a part of the triple diagonal matrix need be formed and the eigenvalues of this converge to the lowest eigenvalues of the system as more of the tri-diagonal is formed. Typically, if m eigenvalues and vectors are required then the first 2mx2m partition of the tri-diagonal matrix is formed and this gives accurate estimates for the first m eigenvalues and associated eigenvectors. As with the subspace iteration method it is very important to enforce the orthogonal characteristics of the transformation vectors to ensure that convergence does not default to only converging on the first eigenvalue. Methods have been developed for the Lanczos technique to identify when re-orthogonalisation is required so that the computational efficiency is improved by only using selective re-othogonalisation as required.

Both the subspace iteration and the Lanczos method have convergence problems associated with them and can miss relevant eigenvalues. The subspace iteration method relies heavily upon the initial starting vectors having components in then that contain parts of the eigenvectors required. Typically, for a cantilever beam problem some modes will be beam bending and some will be axial stretching. If no axial modes are included in the initial choice of vectors (the initial subspace) then they do not get included as a part of the iteration process and no axial modes will be found even when they have eigenvalues in the range of interest. Similarly, if only one axial mode is included in the initial subspace then only one axial resonant frequency will be computed. In practice, for real structures that are geometrically complicated this is not much of a problem. The Lanczos method can suffer from a similar problem if the stiffness matrix of the structure consists of two or more separate uncoupled matrices. The Lanczos method can also have difficulties converging to multiple eigenvalues. If there is an eigenvalue with a multiplicity of three say then the first one of the set is found without difficulty. The second requires more iterations than would be expected if it was only a single root and the third requires more still. The lack of these eigenvalues in both the subspace iteration and the Lanczos methods can be checked for using the Sturm sequence method.

### 2.10.4 Sturm Sequence Methods

The Sturm sequence method only locates eigenvalues and it does it rather differently to all of the other methods discussed so far. A specific number, g, is specified by the user and the Sturm sequence method then computes how many eigenvalues there are below g. It does not compute the eigenvalues themselves but it could be used to do so by systematically choosing a sequence of values for g. Its main strength lies in the fact that it only relies upon the signs of numbers rather than their value and this makes it very well conditioned numerically. However, it is computationally expensive and is rarely used to compute eigenvalues. Instead is is used as a check to confirm that any other method used to find the first m eigenvalues has not missed one or more. Since it is a checking process it is discussed in rather more detail in chapter 8.

## 2.11  Choice  of  Eigenvalue  Extraction  Method

There are many different eigenvalue extraction methods and most systems provide the user with more than one to choose from. Obviously the choice is conditioned by what is available with the system under use but general advice can still be given. If only the lowest eigenvalue is required, say to check that it is above a machines operating speed, then inverse iteration is best. For frequencies other than the fundamental it has convergence problems and should be avoided. If the problem only involves a small number of degrees of freedom then either the QR, the Jacobi or some other form of orthogonalisation transformation technique can be used. Typically a small set such as this can arise if a Guyan reduction process or substructuring has been used. In this case the matrices will tend to be fully populated which makes the transformation methods very attractive. For large sets of equations then either subspace iteration or the Lanczos method should be used. This is the situation most often encountered within a finite element analysis. The efficiency of both the subspace iteration and the Lanczos methods are such that with most modern systems it is better to find the eigenvalues and vectors using the full, uncondensed set of equations rather than to use condensation techniques such as Guyan reduction. The condensation methods introduce errors into the system of computed eigenvalues and vectors and, because they destroy the banding of the equations, they are not computationally efficient.

## 2.12  Direct  Solution  in  the  Frequency  Domain

It is possible to calculate the steady state solution in the frequency domain directly without the eigenvectors having to be found. The equation of motion is

$$\mathbf{M\ddot{r}} + \mathbf{C\dot{r}} + \mathbf{Kr} = (\mathbf{G}_1 + i\,\mathbf{G}_2)e^{i\omega t}$$

This has the response

$$\mathbf{r} = (\mathbf{g}_1 + i\,\mathbf{g}_2)e^{i\omega t}$$

Substituting this into the equation of motion gives

$(K+i\omega C-\omega^2 M)(g_1 + i\ g_2) = (G_1 + i\ G_2)$

This is a set of simultaneous equations with complex coefficients. They can be solved using standard methods such as Gauss elimination to give the response as

$(g_1 + i\ g_2) = (K+i\omega C-\omega^2 M)^{-1}(G_1 + i\ G_2) = H(\omega)(G_1 + i\ G_2)$

Where the dynamic flexibility matrix is

$H(\omega) = (K+i\omega C-\omega^2 M)^{-1}$

and is identical to the modal form of section 2.5 if all of the systems eigenvectors are used. However, the direct form requires a full set of n complex simultaneous equations to be solved which makes it expensive. It also becomes ill conditioned if the excitation frequency, $\omega$, is close to any resonant frequency $\omega j$ and, since the eigenvalues have not been calculated, these regions of ill conditioning are not known. For these reasons this form of solution is not widely used.

## 2.13 Direct Solution in the Time Domain - Step-by-Step Solutions

It is also possible to calculate the response in the time domain without first finding the eigenvalues and the eigenvectors. At some time t it is assumed that the displacement and velocities are known. Using the equation of motion the accelerations are then found as

$\ddot{r} = M^{-1}(R-C\dot{r}-Kr)$

The accelerations are assumed to vary in some way over a small time interval $\Delta t$ so that they can be integrated to find the velocities and displacements at the time $t+\Delta t$. These are then used in the equations of motion to find the response over the next time step.

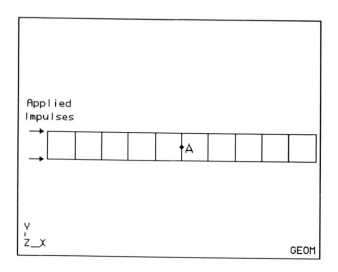

<u>Fig 2.5 - Finite Element Wave Propagation Model</u>

There are many different variations within these step-by-step methods depending upon the assumptions used to integrate the accelerations to find approximations for the velocities and displacements at the end of the step. The various methods are classified in the mathematical sense as either implicit or explicit schemes. If the equilibrium conditions given by the equation of motion are applied at time t at the start of the step then this gives an explicit method. If, however, the equilibrium conditions are used at the time t+Δt at the end of the step then this gives an implicit method. The simple scheme given above is an explicit method. It is found in practice that some methods become numerically unstable if too large a time step is used whilst other methods are stable for any step length. This gives a rather more useful practical classification as methods that are either conditionally stable or that are unconditionally stable. Generally, explicit methods are conditionally stable and implicit methods are unconditionally stable although this is not invariably the case. Unconditionally stable algorithms can only be proved to be always numerically stable for linear problems. There are very many forms of numerical integration schemes for solving the equations of motion. Methods that are commonly encountered as conditionally stable algorithms within finite element systems are:

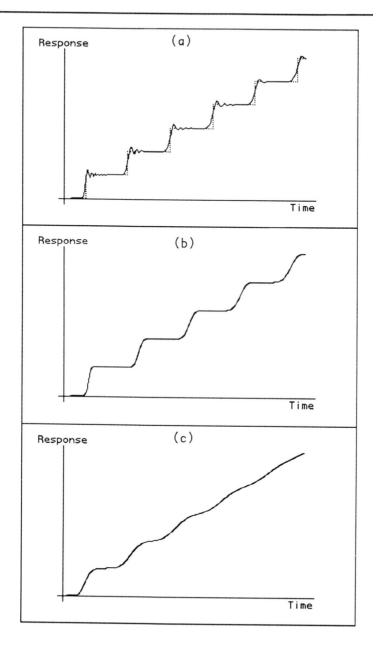

Fig 2.6 - Bar Impulse Response at Point  A

1)  Central difference
2)  Hilber Hughes Taylor

Common unconditionally stable schemes are:

1)  Newmark Beta
2)  Wilson Theta
3)  Houbolt

In both sets the first one listed is the most common variant found within systems. In practice there is not much to choose between the ones listed in each category but conditionally stable and unconditionally stable algorithms do have significantly different advantages and disadvantages.

For any of these methods it is usually best to start the process with one or two time steps where the applied force is zero. Some techniques, especially the higher order integration schemes require special solution steps to start the process and the use of a small number of zero force time steps initially helps to smooth the starting process. If the integration method does require special starting steps the user should avoid sharp or step changes in the input forcing function. A step change implies that an impulse is applied and this should be accompanied by the special starting steps. In this case the forcing function should be made to change smoothly over two or three steps. Simple integration schemes such as the Newmark Beta method do not suffer from this problem and can cope with step changes in the forcing.

*2.13.1 Conditionally Stable Methods*

These methods are computationally very simple. They use the equations of motion in the form

$$\ddot{\mathbf{r}} = \mathbf{M}^{-1}(\mathbf{R} - \mathbf{R}_c - \mathbf{R}_k)$$

Where $\mathbf{M}$ is idealised as being diagonal so that the inverse is trivial. $\mathbf{R}_c$ and $\mathbf{R}_k$ are the damping and stiffness forces respectively. There is no need to form the stiffness and

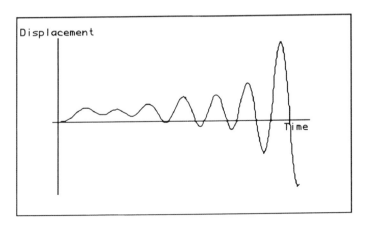

Fig 2.7 - Numerically Unstable Bar Impulse Response

damping matrices explicitly, the forces can be formed on an element basis. This makes the conditionally stable method very economical with computer storage and it is also very suitable for solving non-linear dynamic problems. Very often the damping is numerical rather than real and is used to control spurious high frequency 'ringing' that can occur in the response. A suitable value is often found by numerical experiment, adjusting its value until the response has no significant ringing but is main characteristics are still correct. This is illustrated by the unsupported bar model shown in figure 2.5, which is excited with an impulse at the left hand end causing a step wave to propagate down the bar. If only a very small amount of damping is included in the model then the displacement response; against time at point A is as shown in figure 2.6(a). The exact solution is shown by the dotted line. Point A remains stationary until the wave front caused by the impulse hits it when it jumps to a new position. It stays at this value until the wave reflected at the far end travels back and causes it to jump again. This is repeated each time the reflected wave passes point A.

The bar is unsupported so that it moves to the right but each point does this in a series of jerks as the wave front passes back and forth. It can be seen that the basic response is reproduced by the finite element model but because this only has a finite number of degrees of freedom there is a considerable 'ringing' in the computed response. This ringing can be controlled to some extent by tuning the damping, giving it an increased value. The response shown in figure 2.6(b) is then obtained. It will be seen that this gives a better representation of the step wave front. However, the artificial damping does cause the long term term response to deteriorate. After the wave has been reflected several time from the ends of the bar then as each reflected wave front passes the point A the response is becoming less sharp and more smeared. If the calculation is continued long enough the numerical damping will eventually cause all points on the bar to have the same velocity and the it will move as a rigid body. This is illustrated in figure 2.6(c), where a high value of numerical damping has been used. In all of these three examples the damping is only proportional to the stiffness so that there is no rigid body damping. The use of damping only proportional to stiffness is good for impact problems since it causes the high frequency (less accurate) modes to be more heavily damped than the rather more physically meaningful low frequency ones.

Use of simple pilot studies such as this is a good way to test the solution algorithm and to find suitable numerical damping factors. The geometry is simple, the shape of the exact wave front is simple and well defined and the speed of propagation of the wave can be checked using the material properties.

One problem with conditionally stable algorithms is the choice of the time step $\Delta t$. If it is too large the solution is unstable and the response just increases rapidly with time. This is illustrated in figure 2.7 where the same wave propagation problem has before has been analysed with (just) too large a time step. It will be seen that the solution oscillates with an increasing amplitude. In this case the time step chosen was only slightly greater than that for a stable response so that it takes a number of steps before the error becomes significant but after this it dominates the response. If the time step is too small then a very large number of time steps are required and the solution is computationally expensive. The length of the time step is controlled by the highest natural frequency within the finite element model. If this has a time period T then the required time step is of the order of T/4, depending upon the precise algorithm used. Usually the highest eigenvalue is not known so that this is rarely useful. A more practical method for estimating the time step is, knowing the wave speed of the material from its material properties, the smallest time to propagate a wave between any two nodes is found. The required $\Delta t$ is then somewhere between this and 1/10th of this value depending upon the algorithm.

Conditionally stable algorithms are the best solution technique for non-linear dynamic problems and for linear problems involving impact loading or others forms of loadings that are concentrated in a small area of the structure and change rapidly. These are characterised by the fact that waves are propagated into the body of the structure. They are not well suited to solve problems where the loading changes at a relatively low frequency since these require many time steps. Matrix reduction processes such as Guyan reduction should never be used with conditionally stable algorithms. They decrease the accuracy of the solution and usually cause the cost of the analysis to increase rather than decrease.

*2.13.2 Unconditionally Stable Methods*

For the unconditionally stable methods the solution process is modified so that the response is always numerically stable for any time step value. This does not mean that any time step can be used for any problem since it is found that the accuracy of the solution decreases as the time step is increased. Generally this error occurs in two ways, the effective frequency of the higher modes is reduced (there is a period elongation) and, secondly, artificial damping is introduced that increases with frequency. The time step is chosen in this case by the analyst deciding what is the highest frequency of interest in the force input or the response and then choosing a time step one tenth of the period of this frequency. The error introduced into the frequencies of interest is then negligible.

Unconditionally stable methods are not suitable for solving non-linear problems for two reasons. They are only unconditionally stable for linear problems and can be unstable for non-linear ones depending upon the nature of the non-linearity. In addition, the mathematics involved in making the the process unconditionally stable means that a matrix involving the mass, the damping and the stiffness has to be solved at each time step. This cannot be made diagonal. For linear problems it can be set up once but for non-linear problems it has to be continually reformed which makes the process very expensive computationally. Unconditionally stable methods are suitable for transient problems where the loading is not changing so rapidly that it is an impact problem but where a large number of modes would be required to solve the problem using a modal solution.

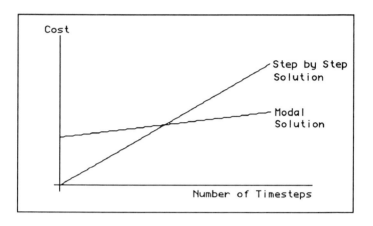

<u>Fig 2.8  - Relative Solution Costs Against Time of Response</u>

## 2.14  Choice of Solution Method

The choice of the solution method depends very much upon the problem under consideration. If the system behaviour is non-linear then the conditionally stable step-by-step integration technique is the only general method available and is almost invariably used. For other problems the choice lies between modal methods and direct solution methods. If the problem is periodic and the steady state solution is required then any step-by-step integration method should be discarded. If there are only one or two fixed frequencies of interest then the direct solution in the frequency domain described in section 2.12. can be considered. However, for most steady state problems it is almost always better to use the modal solution described in section 2.5.

For transient problems the choice is less clear. The cost of a direct step-by-step solution increases linearly with the number of time steps. For a modal solution the eigenvalues and eigenvectors have to be found before any response can be calculated. This means that this initial cost has to be paid and its magnitude depends upon the number of eigenvalues required and the size of the problem. However, once the modes have been found the cost per step is very cheap and large steps can be taken (if the force input; has been idealised as straight line segments so that the convolution integral is evaluated exactly) without any loss of accuracy. These points are illustrated diagrammatically in figure 2.8 It will be seen that for a small number of steps the direct solution is cheaper but there will always come a cross over point where the modal solution is cheaper. If more than one load case has to be solved then the modal solution is much more attractive since the eigenvalues only have to be found once. The cost of the step-by-step solution just accumulates in a linear manner for each load case. For short duration transients where the forces; are localised the step-by-step integration is best. For a more gentle time variation of the force that is spread over the structure or where a series of load cases have to be considered then a modal solution is better.

## 2.15 Reduction of Solution Cost

Any dynamic solution is inevitably more expensive than a static analysis. The extra cost arises from various sources. A mass matrix has to be formed in addition to the stiffness matrix, determination of eigenvectors requires the same amount of computational effort as at least solving for as many load cases as there are eigenvectors and, finally, the response has to be computed at many time steps or frequencies. Ways of conducting the analysis in stages so that the results obtained from one stage can be used to determine the most economical way of computing the next step are discussed in chapter 8. The cost of the analysis will be reduced if the mass matrix is lumped into a diagonal form. This is especially true if a step-by-step numerical integration solution method is used. Many systems work with a diagonal mass matrix by default. In a modal solution care over the choice of the number of modes that are recovered can reduce the cost but, if a significant mode is omitted from the response calculation then accuracy is also lost. There are some techniques available to reduce the problem size, notably the Guyan reduction method described in chapter 5. However, these lead to some loss of accuracy and, if too many reduction vectors are specified, they will not reduce the cost significantly. If the system contains an efficient eigenvalue extraction scheme, such as subspace iteration or the Lanczos method, then it has been noted on some occasions that the use of a matrix reduction process actually increases the analysis cost. These reduction schemes are better suited to the older eigenvalue extraction methods that do not take advantage of the form of the finite element equations. Finally, the correct choice of element types and mesh densities can have a very significant effect upon the analysis cost. These are best investigated by means of simplified pilot studies conducted before the main problem is solved. Such studies and how to make decisions regarding modelling of the main structure and any secondary components are discussed in chapter 3.

# CHAPTER 3 - MODELLING

## 3.1 Introduction

Before considering the finite element aspects of modelling for a dynamic analysis some more general dynamic modelling aspects must be decided upon. As outlined in the previous chapter there are various solution techniques available and the one most appropriate to the problem at hand should be chosen. In addition to this, other questions should be answered at this stage before the actual finite element model is considered. There are various components that are always required by any model for a dynamic analysis, these being:

1) A description of the stiffness or any other mechanism for storing potential energy within the system.
2) A description of the mass for storing potential energy within the system.

These are all that is required for any system to have the potential to vibrate. If only the natural frequencies and mode shapes (the eigenvalues and eigenvectors) are required from the analysis then a description of these two quantities is sufficient. If a forced response is required then other aspects of the problem might have to be defined. These are:

1) The forcing function and how it varies with time or frequency.
2) The initial conditions of displacement and velocity when the force is applied.
3) The damping within the system.
4) The nature of the environment surrounding the structure when it is vibrating.

None of these are necessary for any given vibration problem but some are required by most problems. If the structure has a time varying force then very often the conditions at time zero are that the structure is at rest. Alternatively, there might be no force applied to the structure but there is an initial displacement or velocity. If the force is described in terms of its frequency content (in the frequency domain) then the steady state response is usually required in which case no initial conditions are needed. The damping is discussed in chapter 7 but it is common, as a first approximation and for a conservative response estimate, to assume that the damping is zero. The nature of the environment surrounding the structure needs to be considered since this can affect the dynamic response of the system. If the structure is surrounded by water then this can affect the dynamic response in various ways and these might have to be considered.

## 3.2 Units for a Dynamic Analysis

One problem that is often encountered within a dynamic analysis is the units to be used. The equation of motion

$$\mathbf{M\ddot{r} + C\dot{r} + Kr = R}$$

is just an equation of equilibrium. Each term in the equation must have the same units of force. For the mass term the inertia force is

$$\text{volume} * \text{density} * \text{length} / \text{time}^2 = \text{force}$$

If the units of length are metres, of density kilograms per cubic metre and time is seconds then this has the combined units

$$\text{kilograms metres} / \text{second}^2 = \text{Newtons}$$

If the units of length are changed to millimetres then this becomes

$$\text{kilograms millimetres} / \text{second}^2 = \text{Newtons} * 10^3$$

If all of the other terms have force units of Newtons then the material density in units of kilograms per cubic millimetre must be divided by 1000 to give the required force units of Newtons. That is, for lengths in millimetres the density must be in megagrams per cubic millimetre to give units of Newtons to the force. This is because the unit of force, the

Newton, has the units of length in metres in its definition. Care must always be taken in any dynamic analysis to ensure that consistent units have been used.

In choosing units of length the units consistent with the size of the geometry should be used. If the real structure is small with lengths of a fraction of a metre it is better to use millimetres as the basic units of length. If the real structure is metres in size then the analyst should work in metre lengths. This is especially true if beam or plate elements are to be used where the element freedoms contain both displacements and rotations. If this is the case then changing the units of length used to define the structure changes the relative sizes of the numbers in the stiffness and mass matrices. If a computer with an infinite word length were being used this would make no difference but, with a real finite word length machine, an inappropriate choice of length units can lead to ill-conditioning of the resulting equations.

## 3.3 Primary and Secondary Components

One difference between a static analysis and a dynamic analysis is that it is usually relatively easy to imagine how a loading is carried statically. It is then only necessary to include the relevant portions of the structure within the analysis model. This is nowhere near so easy for a vibration analysis. For dynamics apparently unimportant parts of the structure can have an important effect upon the response. Any real structure is much too complicated to model exactly and some approximations must be made. There is usually one part of the structure that is the reason for conducting the analysis and this is termed the primary component. There will then be other parts of the structure that are not of direct interest but they might be important in the dynamic analysis. These are called the secondary components. The analyst must decide what is the primary and what are the secondary components.

From the point of view of computational efficiency the problem is simplified if the secondary components can be omitted from the model. If they cannot be omitted the next best thing to do is to include them as either mass or stiffness attached to the primary component so that they do not add any extra degrees of freedom. If this is not possible then a dynamic model of the secondary structure must be formed. Note that the primary

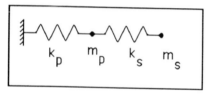

Fig 3.1  Primary and Secondary systems

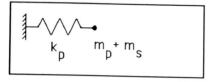

Fig 3.2 - Idealisation when $\omega s > \omega p$

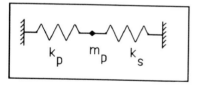

Fig 3.3 - Idealisation when $\omega s < \omega p$

component might be large compared to the secondary components. At one extreme the primary might be a chemical tank and the secondaries are pipes connected to the tank. Alternatively, the primary might be small compared to the secondary, for example it might be a storage tank installed in a flexible building. The tank is the primary component and the building the secondary. What matters from the idealisation point of view is not the mass or stiffness of the primary and secondary components but their relative frequencies. If the resonant frequencies of the two components are comparable then the secondary structure must be modelled as a dynamic component with both the mass and stiffness considered. If the resonant frequencies of the secondary components are greater than those of the primary then they can be modelled as mass added onto the primary. Alternatively, if the resonant frequencies of the secondary components are lower than those of the primaries then they can be modelled as stiffnesses added to the primary.

To illustrate this consider the simple two degree of freedom model shown in figure 3.1. The primary component is represented by the spring of stiffness $k_p$ and the mass $m_p$. The secondary component is represented by the stiffness $k_s$ and the mass $m_s$. Considering the primary component alone then it will have a resonant frequency $\omega_p{}^2 = k_p/m_p$. For the

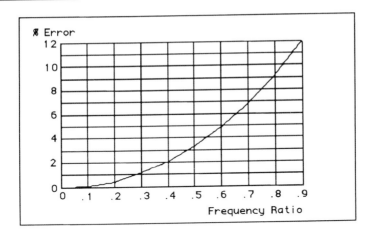

Fig 3.4 - Errors of Simplified Secondary Component Models

secondary component, assuming that the primary is rigid, then it has a resonant frequency $\omega_s^2 = k_s/m_s$.

If $\omega_s > \omega_p$ then the idealisation shown in figure 3.2, where the secondary mass is added to the primary and the secondary stiffness is ignored, is valid. Comparing the error in resonant frequency of the idealised model with the fundamental frequency of the full model shown in figure 3.1 then, for any mass and stiffness values of the secondary the error plot of figure 3.4 is obtained, where the frequency ratio is $\omega_p/\omega_s$. It will be seen from this that for $\omega_s/\omega_p > 2$ the error is always less than 3.5% and it decreases the greater the value of $\omega_s/\omega_p$. Adding the mass of the secondary to the primary is valid when $\omega_s/\omega_p > 2$.

If $\omega_s < \omega_p$ then the idealisation shown in figure 3.3, where the secondary mass is grounded and only the secondary stiffness is included, is valid. Again, comparing the error of this model with the full two degree of freedom system, then the same error plot of figure 3.4 is obtained for any mass or stiffness values. In this case the frequency ratio is $\omega_s/\omega_p$. It will be seen that, again, the error is always less than 3.5% for $\omega_s/\omega_p < 1/2$. Grounding the mass of the secondary is valid when $\omega_s/\omega_p < 1/2$.

A conclusion from this is that if the fundamental frequencies of the primary and secondary components differ by more than a factor of 2 then the simplified representation of the

| $m_s/m_p$ | $\omega_1/\omega$ | $\omega_2/\omega$ |
|---|---|---|
| 1E-5 | .9968 | 1.0032 |
| 5E-5 | .9930 | 1.0071 |
| 1E-4 | .9905 | 1.0101 |
| 5E-4 | .9779 | 1.0226 |
| 1E-3 | .9689 | 1.0732 |
| 5E-3 | .9317 | 1.0732 |
| 1E-2 | .9049 | 1.1051 |
| 5E-2 | .8000 | 1.2500 |
| 1E-1 | .7298 | 1.3701 |
| 5E-1 | .5000 | 2.0000 |
| 1 | .3820 | 2.6180 |

Table 3.1 - Frequency Separation for Coupled Tuned Systems

secondary as added mass or grounded mass can be used as appropriate. Looking at the error curve of figures 3.4 it will be seen that the errors in these simple idealisations increase rapidly as $\omega_s$ becomes equal to $\omega_p$. In this case the simple idealisations of figures 3.2 and 3.3 are not valid and the secondary structure has to be included as a dynamic system with both mass and stiffness. In other words, where the two frequencies differ by a factor between 0.5 and 2, the secondary component is dynamically important and must be included as a part of the primary component. This is true even when the mass of the secondary component is very small, especially when the two frequencies, $\omega_p$ and $\omega_s$, are very close. This is illustrated in table 3.1, where the errors in frequency resulting from ignoring the secondary structure for various values of $m_s/m_p$ are given. it will be seen that there are significant differences even when this ratio is as small as 0.005.

These illustrations are exact for the simple two degree of freedom system of figure 3.1. Obviously, any real structure is much more complicated than this but the observations can be generalised to the more complex case. Two simple models of the primary and secondary structures are constructed. For the primary model the secondary structure is ignored

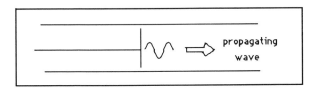

Fig 3.5 - Piston in a Fluid Filled Cylinder

entirely and for the secondary structure it is completely fixed at the points where it connects to the primary. Any natural support points are included in either model as appropriate. The fundamental frequencies of each structure are computed (if the primary has rigid body motions with zero eigenvalues then the first non-zero resonant frequency is considered) and compared on the same basis as the simple two degree of freedom model. This allows an appropriate choice of the modelling of the secondary structure to be made. Only simple models are required because only the fundamental frequencies are needed for the comparisons. However, if simple models are used then it is probably safer to widen the range where the secondary component has to be modelled dynamically to lie within a frequency ratio, $\omega_s/\omega_p$, of 1/3 to 3. If more detailed models are used then the range 1/2 to 2 is valid. The assumption here is that the structure is responding most strongly at its fundamental frequency. This is usually the case but it might not be so if the lowest mode is not excited for some reason. Say, for example, the fundamental is a torsional mode but the loading only induces bending. In this case the frequency of the first significant mode of response of the primary should be considered as the primary frequency. If in doubt it is always safer, but more expensive, to include the secondary component as a part of the dynamic model. A general form of this then becomes dynamic substructuring, as discussed in chapter 5.

## 3.4 The Surrounding Environment

The surrounding environment can also be considered as a secondary component but this can have a different effect than that of a spring mass model. Considering the surrounding

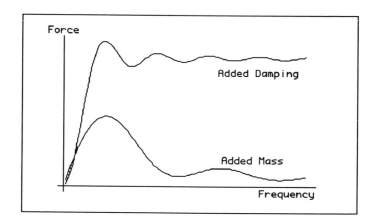

Fig 3.6 - Reaction Forces on a Vibrating Piston

environment as a fluid then a simple model that can be used to investigate its influence is a rigid piston vibrating harmonically at a frequency, $\omega$, in a rigid tube, as shown in figure 3.5. As the piston vibrates it will feel forces exerted on it from the fluid. Since the piston is vibrating harmonically these forces can either be in phase with the movement or ninety degrees out of phase. A plot of the in and out of phase reaction forces against frequency are given in figure 3.6. It will be seen that the in phase component rises to a maximum and then decreases as the frequency is increased. This is interpreted as an effect of the added mass of the fluid on the piston. As the piston oscillates it accelerates some of the fluid backwards and forwards with it. At low frequencies the accelerations are low and hence the added mass forces are also low. At high frequencies the column of air vibrates so that only a thin layer of the fluid is accelerated directly by the piston, the higher the frequency the thinner the layer, so the added mass force decreases at high frequencies. Added mass terms are only important over a restricted frequency range and can be ignored at high frequencies. Also, the magnitude of the added mass terms are proportional to the fluid density so if the fluid is light, such as air, then they can be ignored in relation to the mass of the structure. If the structure is immersed in water then they are likely to be significant since the density of water is so much greater than that of air.

The out of phase component of the reaction force rises as the piston frequency is increased until it reaches a constant value. This component of the force can be interpreted as a damping force on the piston. It arises from the fact that, as the piston vibrates, it generates sound wave in the fluid and this wave travels down the pipe. As the wavefront moves some portion of the fluid that was initially at rest becomes excited and gains energy. This energy comes from the piston and so appears as an apparent damping force on the piston. This is the radiation damping discussed in chapter 7. The radiation damping increases with frequency until the wavefront in the cylinder becomes plane. At high frequencies a plane wave front is developed very near to the piston surface and hence the apparent damping force becomes constant. The simple radiation model discussed in chapter 7 is valid when a plane wave can be developed very close to the structure's surface.

The radiation force is also proportional to the density of the fluid but the effect can be important even for low density fluids, such as air, since the inherent damping within most structures is very low. It is especially important for a denser fluid such as water. The same radiation damping can also occur in solids where it becomes a very efficient damping mechanism. Much of the damping in real structures comes from radiation damping.

If the surrounding fluid has a significant effect both in terms of added mass and added stiffness then it should be included in the dynamic model. If the fluid encloses the structure then this can be done by modelling the fluid as finite elements. If the fluid surrounds the structure and extends, to all intents and purposes, to infinity then it is less appropriate to model it using finite elements alone. In such cases finite elements can be used to model the structure and boundary integral equations to model the infinite fluid. This gives a more appropriate total model. These considerations are important for acoustic problems.

## 4.5 Boundary Conditions and Joints

One of the major problems associated with a dynamic analysis is the modelling of boundary conditions and joints. These are discussed in more detail in the next chapter but it is still worth while emphasising here the difficulties associated with them. A common assumption made with a dynamic model is that a support is rigid. In practice the support will be another system of some description. It will have mass and stiffness and can respond dynamically. Generally a high stiffness is associated with a relatively high mass so that the natural frequencies of the supports can be of the same order as some of the higher important structural frequencies. If this is the case then the supports will not be dynamically rigid and their movement will affect the resonant frequencies of the structure. For design purposes this is probably not too significant but, as discussed in chapter 6, it can be very important when comparing with experimental results.

Similar difficulties can arise with the dynamic behaviour of structural joints. If the joints are flexible then they will have a significant effect on the magnitudes of the lower resonant frequencies. Such joints should be modelled. However, this is easier said than done and in most cases the actual stiffness of the joint is not well defined. Depending upon their nature joints can be modelled as springs connecting nodes together or as reduced stiffness values in the elements on either sides of the joint. Parametric studies can then be conducted, varying the properties of the joints, in order to investigate the sensitivity of the eigenvalues and vectors to the joint idealisation. At the least this will highlight possible modelling difficulties. At best the sensitivity analysis can be used in conjunction with experimental tests to provide realistic parameter values. This is discussed in chapter 6.

Supports and joints can be important sources of damping within a real structure. The various forms of damping that they can give rise to are discussed in chapter 7. The support and joint dampings are rarely modelled in detail since, although they increase the energy dissipation within the structure, the damping is still only a small fraction of critical.

## 3.6  Rotating Structures

Most structures vibrate about a stationary position and the standard equation of motion of the form

$$\mathbf{M}\ddot{\mathbf{r}} + \mathbf{C}\dot{\mathbf{r}} + \mathbf{K}\mathbf{r} = \mathbf{R}(t)$$

assumes this condition. However, there is a significant class of structures that are rotating under their normal operating conditions. These include gas and steam turbines and helicopter blades. The fact that the structure is rotating alters the dynamics characteristics and the equations of motion have to be modified. The equation of motion is just an equation of equilibrium and in the standard form given above states that the sum of the inertia force plus the damping force plus the stiffness force equals the applied force. If the structure rotates then two extra forces need to be included on the left hand side of the equation. These are the centrifugal forces and the Coriolis or gyroscopic forces. They occur as separate terms in the equations and have different consequences on the results. Their magnitude are both defined by the mass distribution in the structure. If the structure rotates there will always be centrifugal forces but the Coriolis forces are not always present.

## 3.6.1 Centrifugal Forces and Stress Stiffening

The centrifugal forces are proportional to the structural displacements and are often called stress stiffening terms since they cause an increase to the total stiffness. The magnitude of these stress stiffening terms are proportional to the square of the speed of rotation of the machine. The equations of motion with centrifugal forces can be written as

$$\mathbf{M\ddot{r} + C\dot{r} + Kr + K_g r = R}$$

where $\mathbf{K_g}$ is the stress stiffening arising from the centrifugal forces. This has the same characteristics as the elastic stiffness matrix and is available in most system either directly or, indirectly, by calculating the geometric stiffness matrix arising from the stresses induced by the structure rotating with a constant angular velocity about a central axis . As the name stress stiffening implies these terms cause the resonant frequencies to increase. If the speed of rotation is very low they have little effect and the resonant frequencies are controlled by the normal elastic stiffness matrix. As the rotation speed increases then the centrifugal forces increase rapidly. If the rotation speed is sufficiently high then the centrifugal forces will dominate over the elastic terms and the structures elastic stiffness becomes insignificant. This is illustrated in figure 3.7, which shows a plot of the fundamental frequency of a gas turbine blade against the speed of rotation of the turbine. It will be seen that when the rotation speed is close to zero then the resonant frequency is substantionally constant. This is where the response is controlled by the elastic stiffness. As the turbine rotation speed increases then the fundamental frequency increases. When the rotation speed is sufficiently high then it can be seen that the resonant frequency increases linearly with the rotation speed. In this regime the centrifugal forces are considerably higher than the elastic stiffness forces.

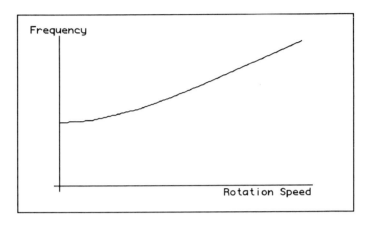

<u>Fig 3.7 - Change of First Resonant Frequency with Speed of Rotation</u>

This form of stress stiffening can occur for any loaded structure that has appreciable volume of material under a membrane stress distribution. The stretching of a drum skin shows this, where the resonant frequency increases as the skin is stretched tighter. For most structures this stress stiffening is very much less than the elastic stiffness and is usually ignored.

### 3.6.2 Coriolis or Gyroscopic Forces

The gyroscopic forces of rotation give rise to different effects than the centrifugal forces. The magnitude of the gyroscopic forces are proportional to the velocity of the structure and, at first sight appear like damping forces. In practice they are very different. The general form for the gyroscopic force is

$$\mathbf{H}\,\dot{\mathbf{r}} = (\mathbf{A} - \mathbf{A}^t)\,\dot{\mathbf{r}}$$

where $\mathbf{A}$ is a square non-symmetric matrix. This form means that the gyroscopic matrix, $\mathbf{H}$ is a skew symmetric matrix where the diagonal terms $H_{ii}$ are all zero and corresponding off diagonal terms are equal and opposite, $H_{ij} = -H_{ji}$. The skew symmetry has various consequences. For a start, it is easy to show that such a form never dissipates any energy and hence is not a damping matrix. Instead it serves to transfer energy from one mode to another. If the phasing of this energy transfer is correct then the modes involved can increase in amplitude in an unbounded manner so that the structure is dynamically unstable. The whirling of shafts is an example of this. The presence of gyroscopic forces can cause the structure to be dynamically unstable over certain speeds of rotation. Centrifugal stress stiffening is almost always beneficial dynamically since it causes the resonant frequencies to increase. Gyroscopic terms tend to have the reverse effect and can give rise to catastrophic dynamic failure. The gyroscopic terms are usually difficult to include within most finite element packages since these almost invariably assume that the coefficient matrices are symmetric and hence they cannot handle a skew symmetric form. They also lead to a non-standard eigenvalue problem which has to be solved using the techniques for general non-proportional damping as discussed in chapter 7.

## 3.7 Record of Assumptions

As with all aspects of any dynamic analysis (or any form of structural analysis for that matter) the assumptions made at the modelling stage, together with reasons for their choice, should be clearly recorded. These assumptions include such things as what the primary structure actually consists of and what constitutes the secondary structures. The tests used to define the level of modelling required for the secondary structure, as described in section 3.3 should be clearly recorded. Although the main purpose of the analysis is to compute the response, either in terms of displacements or stresses, of the primary structure it is also possible to recover the response of the secondary structures. This is done by taking the computed responses of the primary structure at the attachment points of the secondaries and then applying these as base excitations to the secondary components. If the resonant frequencies of the primary and the secondary structures are sufficiently well separated (they differ by more than a factor of 2) then the secondary response will be reasonably accurate.

The loading is also subject to various forms of idealisation, not the least being that it is often not well defined and some guessing or intuition is needed to decided upon the loads. For real structures there might be many actual load cases that should be considered, but it would be impractical to do so for cost and time considerations. If only a subset of the possible loading cases are selected for dynamic analysis, based upon the judgment that these envelope the worst cases, then the loadings that have actually been chosen together with those that have been discarded should be clearly recorded. Either as the analysis progresses or at its end the choice of load cases should be reviewed in the light of the results that are obtained. It is possible that one or more of the discarded load cases might have characteristics that make it more severe and these should be included in the analysis set.

If the loading includes base movement loads, typical of seismic analysis, then it is possible to calculate the structural response either relative to the base movement or in absolute terms relative to a fixed frame of reference. The final results should obviously be the same but their interpretation and intermediate processing can be different so it is important to make clear and record exactly what is being done. For a seismic analysis, if the input is in terms of a base acceleration time history then this should be baseline corrected to ensure that there is no residual velocity or displacement of the structure at the end of the event. This could arise from the digitisation of the seismic event or from interpolation within time steps used in the response time integration routines. If the input is a time history but it has to represent a defined response spectrum then the match between the defined spectrum and the one calculated from the time history should be recorded.

## 3.8  Mass  Considerations

The considerations for the definition of the stiffness is very similar to those required for a static analysis. If a dynamic stress analysis is to be conducted then the same static analysis model can probably be used for the dynamic analysis. If only the natural frequencies or just the displacement response is required then a much simpler model than that used for a stress analysis is sufficient. For a dynamic analysis, consideration has also to be given to the modelling of the mass distribution. As discussed in the next chapter the mass idealisation can usually be much cruder than that for the stiffness with no significant loss of accuracy.

One new problem that occurs with the mass definition is that most structures are designed to carry some loading and this can often involve large values of non-structural mass. This can lead to various modelling problems. If the non-structural mass is a small fraction of the structural mass then it can be modelled relatively simply as either point masses at some nodes or in terms of modified material densities for some members. If the mass is a significant proportion of the structural mass, sometimes it is greater than the structural mass, then its modelling requires a more detailed consideration. It is especially important to ensure that the centre of gravity of heavy masses are positioned correctly. If this is away from a structural node then it will introduce inertia coupling between degrees of freedom that is not present in a static analysis. Typically, for a beam, masses that have a centre of gravity offset from the beams neutral axis can cause bending and membrane or bending and torsion modes to be coupled. This offset can be modelled in various ways. Where ever possible the analyst should try to place a node at the centre of gravity of any heavy mass, irrespective of whether it is structural or non-structural. This is usually feasible for masses that have stiffness associated with them but not for the non-structural mass. The next best alternative is to place a node at the centre of gravity of the non-structural mass even though this has no stiffness associated with it. The mass node is then coupled to the structure by means of generalised constraints. A similar result can be achieved with elements that have rigid offsets, where the element degrees of freedom can be offset from the neutral axis. Rigid offsets are available in some systems for beam elements and, rather more rarely, for plate and shell elements. Another technique that is available for modelling the offset position of a mass is to connect the node at the centre of gravity of the rigid mass to a structural node by means of an artificial rigid element. This should only be used as a last resort since it effects the numerical conditioning of the resulting equations and can introduce numerical errors. It is also difficult to choose a reasonable value for the artificial stiffness. If it is too low then the connection is no longer rigid and if it is too high the numerical conditioning of the equations becomes such that the solution fails.

Care must be taken when combining approximations associated with the mass matrix. Using rigid offsets and some forms of implementation of multi-point constraints to include the effect of an offset mass must lead to a non-diagonal mass matrix. The off-diagonal terms define the position of the centre of gravity of the mass relative to the connection point. If, as a part of the solution process, the mass matrix is forced to be diagonal then removing the off-diagonal terms corresponds physically to repositioning the centre of gravity of the added mass. This causes a different mass distribution from the one intended to be used in the analysis. If the added mass is large then this can introduce considerable errors.

## 3.9  Loading  Considerations

For a dynamic analysis there are usually three types of loadings that are important:

1) Mechanical forces such as point loads and pressures that vary with time.
2) Base or support movements, defined in terms acceleration or displacement time histories.
3) The structure is released from some initially deformed shape with specified initial displacements or velocities.

Obviously any combination of these can also occur. For a linear analysis each load case can be analysed separately and superposition used to find the response to combined loadings. Modal solutions and solutions in the frequency domain automatically assume that the problem is linear and that the principle of superposition is valid.

Other loadings that can be important for statics are not usually important for dynamics. Typically, thermal loads generally change so slowly that they can be considered as static loads for a dynamic response. Even for thermal transient calculations the time variation can usually be ignored for stressing purposes and the temperature distribution at any time being used as if it were constant.

### 3.9.1 Mechanical Forces

These loads should be applied to the structure using kinematically equivalent loads exactly as for a static analysis. Some of the existing finite element systems only allow dynamic loads to be applied in terms of point loads at nodes. It can then become cumbersome to apply distributed loadings, such as pressure loads, especially for the higher order elements since kinematically equivalent loads should be computed. If statically, rather than kinematically equivalent, loads are used the response at any time will be correct on average but there can be variations in its distribution over the structure, exactly as for a static response. This is not very significant for a displacement response but can cause large stress variations over an element. Where ever possible it is better to use kinematically equivalent loads.

### 3.9.2 Base and Support Movements

There are various degrees of approximation and methods of application for base and support movements available in different systems. Consider the simple frame shown in figure 3.8. This has two support positions, one at either end of the frame. Any form of support movement can be applied if the response is measured relative to some absolute fixed frame of reference. Say the displacements (and the velocities and accelerations) are partitioned into the known base movements $r_b$ and the unknown internal movements $r_i$. The equations of motion can then be partitioned in the same way to give:-

$$M_{ii}\ddot{r}_i + M_{ib}\ddot{r}_b + C_{ii}\dot{r}_i + C_{ib}\dot{r}_b + K_{ii}r_i + K_{ib}r_b = 0$$

$$M_{bi}\ddot{r}_i + M_{bb}\ddot{r}_b + C_{bi}\dot{r}_i + C_{bb}\dot{r}_b + K_{bi}r_i + K_{bb}r_b = R_b$$

Here, $R_b$ are the unknown reaction forces at the base. The base displacements, $r_b$, have a known time history. They can be differentiated to give the base velocities $\dot{r}_b$ and these can be differentiated to give the base accelerations $\ddot{r}_b$ (alternatively if the base accelerations are given then these can be integrated to give the base velocities and displacements). Taking the first equation of the above set this can be rewritten as

$$M_{ii}\ddot{r}_i + C_{ii}\dot{r}_i + K_{ii}r_i = - M_{ib}\ddot{r}_b - C_{ib}\dot{r}_b - K_{ib}r_b = R_i'$$

The right hand side of the equations can be represented by the equivalent dynamic force $R_i'$ and this is known at all time. The equations of motion defined by $M_{ii}$, $C_{ii}$ and $K_{ii}$ can then be solved by any relevant technique to give the absolute response $r_i$. Considering the equivalent force, $R_i'$, then there are usually various simplifications that can be employed.

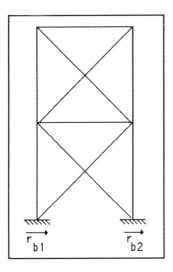

Fig 3.8 - Frame With Base Movements

For most structural problems the damping is so small that the damping component of the force, $C_{ib}\dot{r}_b$, can be ignored. Further, if the mass matrix has been idealised to be a diagonal matrix then the term $M_{ib}$ will be zero. Under these assumptions the equivalent dynamic force is simply

$$R_i' = - K_{ib}r_b$$

so that only the time history of the base displacements need be applied.

Once the structural response $r_i$, $\dot{r}_i$ and $\ddot{r}_i$ have been found at any time then the second equation of the set can be used to compute the base reaction forces $R_b$. This solution method is quite general and will be valid even if the two supports are moving with different time histories. Although this method is the completely general form of solution it is not available in most systems. Instead some other approximate form is used

One simplification that is very often used is to assume that all of the base movements in a given direction are identical, that is the base supports cannot move independently. This tends to arise with seismic problems but not in other cases. Say that the base movement in the i'th direction is $\alpha$ then the movement of the structure relative to the base is:

$$s = r_i - \alpha r_{io} \qquad ; \qquad 0 = r_b - \alpha r_{bo} \quad ; \quad r_o^t = [\, r_{io}^t \quad r_{bo}^t \,]$$

Where $r_o$ is the rigid body movement in the j'th direction. Manipulating the equations using the fact that $Kr_o = 0$ and assuming that the mass and damping matrices are diagonal (or at least there is no coupling to the support freedoms from these) then the equation of motion for the response relative to the supports is

$$M_{ii}\ddot{s} + C_{ii}\dot{s} + K_{ii}s = -\alpha M_{ii}r_{io}$$

which allows the relative base response to be found. This is the form commonly found in programs since it can be used most easily for seismic analysis. As stated before, it is only valid if all of the supports move in an identical manner. Note that the dynamic equations to be solved are identical for both the absolute and the relative response calculations, that is they have the same resonant frequencies and mode shapes. This is to be expected. They only differ in terms of the applied loadings. Within the assumption of $M_{ib} = 0$ then the absolute response can be found by applying a base displacement and the relative response can be found by applying a base acceleration. Provided that the various assumptions are satisfied then the two solution methods will give identical results for stresses and the displacements only differ by a rigid body movement.

A third technique is used in some systems by modifying the equations. Say the base accelerations are known as $\ddot{b}$ then the terms $\beta M_{bb}\ddot{b}$ can be added to both sides of the basic equation. $\beta$ is some arbitrary factor, typically $10^6$. The equations of motion then become:

$$M_{ii}\ddot{r}_i + \qquad M_{ib}\ddot{r}_b + C_{ii}\dot{r}_i + C_{ib}\dot{r}_b + K_{ii}r_i + K_{ib}r_b = 0$$

$$M_{bi}\ddot{r}_i + (1+\beta)M_{bb}\ddot{r}_b + C_{bi}\dot{r}_i + C_{bb}\dot{r}_b + K_{bi}r_i + K_{bb}r_b = R_b + \beta M_{bb}\ddot{b}$$

These equations are solved as defined, including the terms involving the factor $\beta$. Provided that the factor is large then the response will be such that $\ddot{r}_b = \ddot{b}$ and the correct base movements are recovered. The internal response will then be the same as for the previous forms of solution. The main problem associated with this solution strategy is that it involves a loss of numerical conditioning and hence accuracy in the response. If $\beta$ is $10^6$ then this is equivalent to losing about six significant figures in the definition of the mass and stiffness matrices and the chance of numerical rounding errors occurring is increased significantly. If the time history of the displacements is given rather than the accelerations then a similar solution strategy can be adopted but adding stiffness terms a $\mathbf{K_{bbb}}$ to both sides of the equations. Since most eigenvalue extraction schemes involve factorising the stiffness matrix this is likely suffer even more from numerical ill-conditioning.

### 3.9.3 Initial Displacements and Velocities

One further type of dynamic loading is where there structure has some defined displacements or velocities at time zero but these points are free to vibrate thereafter. Say the initial displacements are $\mathbf{r_0}$ and the initial velocities are $\dot{\mathbf{r}}_0$ this implies that the initial accelerations must be

$$\ddot{\mathbf{r}}_0 = \mathbf{M}^{-1} ( \mathbf{R_0} - \mathbf{C}\dot{\mathbf{r}}_0 - \mathbf{Kr_0})$$

where $\mathbf{R_0}$ are the applied forces at time zero. Any solution scheme must use these consistent accelerations to produce the correct results.

If the solution being used involves a step-by-step integration with the full set of equations there is no difficulty in applying the initial displacements or velocities. If any form of condensation has been used, either a Guyan reduction or a reduced modal set then there are some difficulties since an arbitrary set of displacements or velocities can no longer be applied. Typically, for a modal reduction say that the first p modes have been used and these are specified by the eigenvector matrix $\phi$. The full set of dynamic equations are

$$\mathbf{M}\ddot{\mathbf{r}} + \mathbf{C}\dot{\mathbf{r}} + \mathbf{Kr} = \mathbf{0}$$

In this case it is assumed that there are no applied forces but their presence makes no difference. The modal transformation

$r = \phi q$

is defined to condense the equations and these are solved for in terms of the generalised coordinates $q$. If there are initial displacements $r_0$ and initial velocities $\dot{r}_0$ at time zero then

$r_0 = \phi q_0$   and   $\dot{r}_0 = \phi \dot{q}_0$

If a full set of vectors are used $\phi$ is a square non-singular matrix and can be inverted to allow $q_0$ and $\dot{q}_0$ to be found hence defining the initial conditions for the modal equations. If a condensed set of modes has been computed then $\phi$ will be a rectangular matrix and cannot be inverted exactly. Some form of generalised inverse must be applied and advantage can be taken of the orthogonality properties of the vectors since

$\phi^t M \phi = m$

Where $m$ is the diagonal modal mass matrix. If $\phi$ has been mass normalised then $m$ is a unit matrix. Multiplying throughout by $m^{-1}$ this becomes

$m^{-1} \phi^t M \phi = I$

so that an approximate value for the inverse of $\phi$ is $m^{-1} \phi^t M$. The initial modal displacements and velocities can then be taken as

$q_0 = m^{-1} \phi^t M r_0$   and   $\dot{q}_0 = m^{-1} \phi^t M \dot{r}_0$

If these are substituted back then the original values of $r_0$ and $\dot{r}_0$ are not necessarily recovered exactly but only approximately. This approximate inverse is the best method for finding the initial modal conditions. If a modal solution or a Guyan reduction is used then the analyst must not expect the specified initial conditions to be recovered exactly, except for the special case where they are both zero.

---

*3.9.4 Application of an Impulse*

An impulsive load can be applied to a structure by specifying an initial velocity to the nodes that are impulsively loaded. If a set of impulses are applied at various points then these can be described by the vector **P**. The impulse causes a change of momentum. If the structure is at rest before the impulses are applied then the velocity distribution is $\dot{r}_O$ immediately after the impulses. The impulse causes a change of momentum given by

$$M\dot{r}_O = P$$

solving these equations gives the initial velocities as

$$\dot{r}_O = M^{-1}P$$

The initial modal velocities are

$$\dot{q}_O = m^{-1}\phi^t\,M\,\dot{r}_O = m^{-1}\phi^t\,M\,M^{-1}P = m^{-1}\phi^t\,P$$

## 3.10 Frequency Range or Time Steps for the Analysis

When calculating a dynamic response the user needs to specify in some way the significant time intervals for the response. This can be done in one of two ways depending upon the methods used to calculate the response. If a step-by-step numerical integration is being used this is done in terms of the integration time step length. If the response is in terms of a frequency domain solution then it is implied by the frequency range that the analyst chooses. If a modal solution is being used either in the time or frequency domain the shortest time interval over which the response calculation is significant (the highest frequency of significance) is defined by the number of modes used in the analysis. In this case the frequency of the highest mode used is the controlling factor.

*3.10.1 Choice of Frequency Range*

The dynamic characteristics of the forcing function are defined by its frequency content. If the problem to be solved is essentially an impact or impulsive type of load then a step-by-

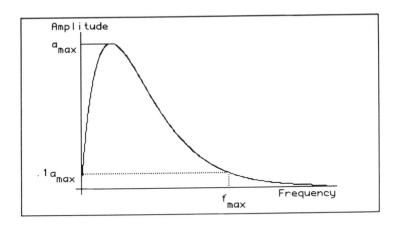

Fig 3.9 - Typical Response Spectrum

step solution method is most convenient. The time step used should be less than the smallest time taken for a wave to propagate between any two nodes. The time step used is normally some where between 1/10th and 1 of this propagation time depending upon the precise solution method used. If the problem is linear then this time step is always used. For non-linear problems it can vary from step to step depending upon the strength of the non-linearities.

In other cases it is not so clear cut as to what time step to take or the number of modes to use. Before the response is found the time content of the loading can be investigated by carrying out a Fourier analysis on it or by finding its response spectrum. These two quantities are closely related and they both define the frequency range within the forcing function. A response spectrum has the shape something of the form shown in figure 3.9. If the amplitude of the force reaches a peak with an amplitude $a_{max}$ then a cut off frequency can be defined as being $\alpha a_{max}$, where, typically, $\alpha=0.1$. Any frequency greater than this has a relatively small force input and can be ignored. In this case the integration time step used is typically $0.1/f_{max}$ and the highest mode to be used is the first mode with a resonant frequency greater than $f_{max}$ Hz. If the Fourier analysis or the response spectrum has the characteristic of becoming constant then the time step can be chosen using the time for a wave to propagate between any two nodes. If a modal solution is being used then the

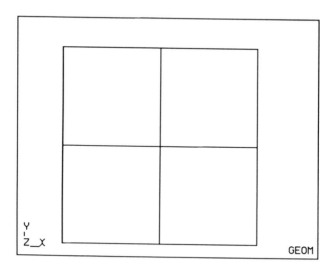

Fig 3.10 - Example Panel for Participation Test

number of modes can be chosen using the technique discussed in section 3.10.2. In this case the time step can be as discussed above but with $f_{max}$ being the resonant frequency of the highest mode used.

Neither the Fourier analysis nor the displacement response spectrum will increase with very high frequencies since this would imply that the energy that can be supplied by the forcing function is infinite and physically this can never be so.

*3.10.2 Number of Modes Required in a Dynamic Analysis*

The number of modes required in a dynamic analysis depends upon the frequency content in the time history of the force and also the way that the force is distributed over the structure. The more uniformly distributed the loading the fewer the number of modes that are required. If the forcing function is of the form $R_0a(t)$, where $R_0$ is the spatial distribution of the force and a(t) is a scalar function of its time history then it can be shown that :

$$\frac{\sum\limits_{i=1}^{p} (\phi_i^t R_O)^2}{(R_O^t M^{-1} R_O)} > 1$$

as the number of modes, p, in the series is increased. The series converges monotonically so that a good representation of the spatial distribution of the force is obtained if the number of modes, $\phi_i$, that is taken is sufficient to make

$$\sum\limits_{i=1}^{p} (\phi_i^t R_O)^2 > c (R_O^t M^{-1} R_O)$$

Where c is some number close to 1, typically 0.9. For a seismic analysis this becomes the mass participation factor.

To illustrate the use of this consider the membrane plate shown in figure 3.10. The number of modes required has been investigated for three load cases

1) Self weight, corresponding to a seismic analysis.
2) A uniform edge pressure along one edge.
3) A point load at the centre of one edge.

The mass participation for the first twenty modes for these three load cases are shown in table 3.2. It will be seen that, as the load becomes more concentrated, then more modes are required to describe its variation over the structure. For the self weight case 99.4% of the mass is participating and 78.9% occurs in the first mode. For the second load case 35.6% of the mass is participating in the first twenty modes and for the point load only 17.9% of the mass is participating.

```
--------------------------------------------------------------------
                 MASS PARTICIPATION LOAD CASE   1
     SELF WEIGHT                           19:35:19  2/ 7/90
   MODE      EIGENVALUE     MODAL FORCE    PARTICIPATION
--------------------------------------------------------------------

    1      3.2195E+05      9.8625E+02         .7980
    2      9.2201E+05      2.3804E+02         .0465
    3      1.6988E+06      4.0936E+02         .1375
    4      1.1110E+07     -5.5659E+01         .0025
    5      1.2590E+07     -2.6954E+00        0.0000
    6      1.3467E+07     -5.5287E+01         .0025
    7      1.7473E+07     -5.2733E+00        0.0000
    8      2.3738E+07     -5.0154E+01         .0021
    9      2.4754E+07      3.6136E+01         .0011
   10      3.3613E+07     -5.5097E+01         .0025
   11      4.1076E+07      2.4470E-01        0.0000
   12      5.2391E+07     -1.8093E+01         .0003
   13      6.4663E+07      4.6297E-02        0.0000
   14      6.9888E+07     -1.9227E+01         .0003
   15      7.5955E+07      1.8731E+01         .0003
   16      7.7828E+07     -6.6718E+00        0.0000
   17      8.8616E+07      1.5181E+01         .0002
   18      9.3117E+07     -2.4228E+00        0.0000
   19      1.0626E+08      2.1185E+01         .0004
   20      1.2812E+08     -6.9892E+00        0.0000

PERCENTAGE OF ACTIVE MASS PATICIPATING........  99.4%
```

Table 3.2 - Participation Factors for Various Loadings

```
--------------------------------------------------------------------
                     MASS PARTICIPATION LOAD CASE    2
        EDGE PRESSURE                            19:39:40   2/ 7/90
   MODE        EIGENVALUE      MODAL FORCE     PARTICIPATION
--------------------------------------------------------------------

    1         3.2195E+05      3.3414E+00         .0518
    2         9.2201E+05      8.0210E-01         .0030
    3         1.6988E+06      1.3139E+00         .0080
    4         1.1110E+07     -7.0366E-01         .0023
    5         1.2590E+07     -3.3702E+00         .0527
    6         1.3467E+07     -1.3120E+00         .0080
    7         1.7473E+07      3.3011E-01         .0005
    8         2.3738E+07      3.0955E+00         .0445
    9         2.4754E+07     -4.1519E-01         .0008
   10         3.3613E+07      1.7351E+00         .0140
   11         4.1076E+07     -2.0927E-01         .0002
   12         5.2391E+07      9.8929E-01         .0045
   13         6.4663E+07     -8.3538E-02        0.0000
   14         6.9888E+07      3.7624E-01         .0007
   15         7.5955E+07     -1.8412E+00         .0157
   16         7.7828E+07      7.4302E-01         .0026
   17         8.8616E+07      5.3433E+00         .1325
   18         9.3117E+07     -2.2281E-01         .0002
   19         1.0626E+08      1.6136E+00         .0121
   20         1.2812E+08     -6.8076E-01         .0022
```

PERCENTAGE OF ACTIVE MASS PATICIPATING........  35.6%

Table 3.2(cont) - Participation Factors for Various Loadings

---

```
                        MASS PARTICIPATION LOAD CASE    3
        POINT LOAD                                19:40: 3  2/ 7/90
   MODE        EIGENVALUE       MODAL FORCE     PARTICIPATION
```

---

| MODE | EIGENVALUE | MODAL FORCE | PARTICIPATION |
|------|-----------|-------------|---------------|
| 1 | 3.2195E+05 | 7.8381E-01 | .0075 |
| 2 | 9.2201E+05 | 1.9796E-01 | .0005 |
| 3 | 1.6988E+06 | 4.6178E-01 | .0026 |
| 4 | 1.1110E+07 | 4.1455E-03 | 0.0000 |
| 5 | 1.2590E+07 | -1.2426E+00 | .0188 |
| 6 | 1.3467E+07 | 1.4925E-01 | .0003 |
| 7 | 1.7473E+07 | -4.5467E-01 | .0025 |
| 8 | 2.3738E+07 | 1.4450E-01 | .0003 |
| 9 | 2.4754E+07 | 8.5550E-01 | .0089 |
| 10 | 3.3613E+07 | 1.4550E+00 | .0258 |
| 11 | 4.1076E+07 | -7.6070E-01 | .0070 |
| 12 | 5.2391E+07 | 9.1545E-01 | .0102 |
| 13 | 6.4663E+07 | -8.2816E-02 | .0001 |
| 14 | 6.9888E+07 | -1.9824E+00 | .0479 |
| 15 | 7.5955E+07 | -3.2756E-01 | .0013 |
| 16 | 7.7828E+07 | 3.9044E-02 | 0.0000 |
| 17 | 8.8616E+07 | 1.3424E+00 | .0219 |
| 18 | 9.3117E+07 | -6.2479E-02 | 0.0000 |
| 19 | 1.0626E+08 | 5.5308E-01 | .0037 |
| 20 | 1.2812E+08 | -1.2772E+00 | .0199 |

PERCENTAGE OF ACTIVE MASS PATICIPATING........ 17.9%

Table 3.2(cont) - Participation Factors for Various Loadings

*3.10.3 Appropriateness of a Modal Solution*

If the frequency content of the time history component of the forcing function falls rapidly with frequency the number of modes required will be defined by the cut off frequency in the forcing function. If the frequency content does not fall off then the number of modes required will be defined by the convergence of the spatial distribution discussed in section 3.10.2. At one extreme, for a seismic analysis, the loads are uniformly distributed and the excitation frequency cuts off at about 30hz so that the number of modes required is very low. At the other extreme a point impact load requires a large number of modes for the spatial description and has a high frequency content. Under both criteria a large number of modes are required and a modal solution is probably inappropriate and, as in done in current practice, a step-by-step integration scheme should be used.

## 3.11  Correlation with Tests

The use of experimental results and methods for correlating between test and theory are discussed in detail in chapter 6. However, it is worth point out here that if it is known that test work is to be conducted at some stage then this should be taken into consideration when designing the dynamic model. The obvious points such as agreeing where the experimental results will be measured should be considered in order that the finite element model can have nodes at these points. However, other points should also be considered such as how the test model is being supported and how it is being excited. It is quite possible that two models are appropriate, one the model used for the design analysis and the second, a modified version of this, to conform more exactly to the test situation. If such care is not taken then a great deal of time and money can be wasted by not comparing similar analytical and experimental models.

## 3.12  Use of Pilot Studies

It is very difficult to build a good dynamic model from scratch even by a highly experienced analyst. A dynamic analysis is expensive to run and can produce a very large amount of output. For these reasons it is always a good idea to construct some simple pilot models to investigate the dynamic behaviour before the full model is formed. This has already been partly discussed and is implied in section 3.3, where the division of a structure into primary and secondary components was considered. Here simplified models of what is intended to be the primary structure and what is being taken as the secondary structures should be built so that the possibility of their dynamic interaction can be investigated. It is at this stage that an appropriate primary model can be defined. Also the example given in section 2.13.1 gives a typical example of a pilot study used for investigating impact and wave propagation problems.

Pilot studies using simple models can also be invaluable for helping to define the important parameters for a dynamic model. They can be used to investigate the range of important frequencies and hence the required number of modes and appropriate solution methods. Being simple models they are also easier to comprehend and allow the analyst to have confidence that he understands the problem. They also provide a knowledge of what is to be expected in the final complete model. This is very useful for guarding against silly mistakes or numerical conditioning problems.

Pilot studies are also extremely useful in investigating the sensitivity of the dynamic response to detailed modelling. The effects of, and sensitivity to, joints can be found thereby allowing the analyst to make a choice of how to model such details and to request supplementary dynamic tests to be conducted if required. Similarly the sensitivity of the support modelling can be investigated. Most dynamic analyses are not very sensitive to precise geometric shape modelling and pilot studies can be used to find what liberties can be taken with the geometrical description without losing accuracy significantly. Similarly it is often possible to lump some details into a single component and the accuracy of such models should be looked at before they are used. A typical example of this is the modelling of a bundle of a large number of tubes in a boiler into a single equivalent beam. If each tube is modelled in detail there will be many degrees of freedom and possibly many close or equal modes that can be lumped into one with no significant loss of accuracy.

Pilot studies can also highlight possible inefficiencies within a model. One example of this was a building analysis where each floor panel was modelled as plate elements. It turned out that these vibrated at much lower frequencies than the overall structure response so that there were some two hundred local panel frequencies before the first main structural frequency. In this case the floor panels were so flexible that they dynamically isolated themselves and could be omitted from the model or treated as simplified secondary components. A few simple pilot models would have highlighted this before a very expensive analysis was conducted.

The volume of data produced by a dynamic analysis can also be controlled by the use of simple pilot studies. These can be used to identify frequency or time periods of the response that are important and the positions in the structure that have the largest displacements and stresses. A knowledge of these allows the user to edit the response that is produced or to tell him where to look when investigating the response using interactive graphics. This is discussed in chapter 8.

# CHAPTER 4 - FINITE ELEMENT MODELLING

## 4.1 Introduction

The considerations required for defining meshes for a finite element dynamic analysis are rather different from those for a static analysis. For statics it is usually not too difficult, with a little experience, to guess which load cases are likely to lead to the highest stresses and where these high stresses are likely to occur. These estimates are then used by the analyst to guide how the mesh is generated and where the mesh is made fine and where it can be coarse. There is often only a limited number of load cases to be considered and the general scope of the analysis can be appreciated before it is started. This is not the case for dynamics. For a start the dynamic response depends not only upon the distribution of the loading over the structure, in the same way as the static analysis does, but it also depends upon how the load varies with time. This is further complicated by the way that the structure itself behaves under dynamic loadings. Generally, with a static analysis, it is possible to imagine how the structure will deflect under a given loading, at least in general terms. This is not the case with dynamics where the interaction between the stiffness and inertia forces will lead to deflected shapes that can be very different from what is expected in statics. For dynamics it is not only necessary to consider the modelling aspects associated with the stiffness distribution in the structure but also the mass distribution has now to be considered.

## 4.2 General Considerations

When considering how to construct a finite element mesh for a dynamic analysis there are a range of aspects of the problem that have to be considered. The stiffness distribution is important, as it is for a static analysis but now so is the mass distribution. For a dynamic analysis the distribution of loads and their time variation must also be considered Finally, the requirements of the result of the analysis can be different for statics and dynamics. Very often the purpose of the static analysis is to find peak stress values associated with stress concentrations. For a dynamic analysis the stress distribution is often less important than knowing the resonant frequencies or the displacements associated with the dynamic response. In some cases a model is constructed initially for a static analysis and this is then picked up and used for a dynamic analysis, often with some form of condensation or reduction process used to reduce the number of degrees of freedom. Often this is a valid thing to do but in some cases the requirements for the dynamic analysis are such that the use of a model designed entirely for static stress analysis can severely compromise the accuracy of the dynamic response. In such cases a specific mesh for dynamics has to be constructed. If a dynamic mesh is constructed from scratch then it generally looks different from one used for static analysis. The dynamic response tends to be distributed more evenly over the structure so that a dynamic mesh is more regular than a static one where the emphasis is put upon placing a fine mesh where the stresses are high.

## 4.3 The Rayleigh Quotient

In order to design a mesh the analyst must have some idea in his mind of the manner in which the structure will respond. For statics experience and common sense can be used to estimate where the stresses are highest for a given loading and what the likely deformed shape will be. The only thing that might require specific investigation is the element size and density needed to recover stresses to the required accuracy. The dynamic behaviour of a structure is such that what is common sense for statics might have no relevance, or be positively misleading, for dynamics. For a structure whose response is linear or mildly non-linear then it can be shown that the total dynamic response is the sum of the modal responses. The resonant frequencies of the modes increase with mode number and one consideration to be used by the analyst is what is the order of magnitude of the highest frequencies that need be considered when calculating the response and how does this affect the choice of modelling. This can be discussed in general terms by means of the Rayleigh quotient. If the structure has a displaced shape, $r$, at any time then the Rayleigh quotient, $Q$, is defined as

$$Q = \frac{r^t K r}{r^t M r}$$

Further, if the minimum values of the Rayleigh quotient are determined, that is the values of the displaced shape, $\mathbf{r}$, for which $dQ/d\mathbf{r}$ is zero then it is found that the corresponding displaced shapes are the eigenvectors and the Rayleigh quotient values the eigenvalues. The first minimum of Q gives the first eigenvalue, the second minimum the second eigenvalue and so on. This is useful because physical meanings can be placed on the terms in the Rayleigh quotient, allowing practical arguments to be made about to find the minima and hence define the mesh.

The top line of the Rayleigh quotient is $\mathbf{r}^t\mathbf{Kr}$ and if this is multiplied by a half then it is the strain energy in the structure. The bottom line is $\mathbf{r}^t\mathbf{Mr}$ which has no immediate physical meaning. However, if the structure is responding harmonically then the displacement is proportional to the velocity and $\mathbf{r}^t\mathbf{Mr}$ can be considered as the kinetic energy in the system. This is not exactly true but for the purposes of the following discussion the terms strain energy and kinetic energy will be used to refer to the top and bottom lines respectively of the Rayleigh quotient.

The absolute minimum of the Rayleigh quotient, that is the lowest resonant frequency, can then be found by minimising the strain energy and maximising the kinetic energy. This is achieved if the structure undergoes gentle variations in the displacements so that the strains, and hence the strain energy, are low but having large overall displacements so that most of the mass of the structure is moving and the kinetic energy is high. This interpretation explains the mode shapes that are observed for structural vibrations.

Consider the mode shapes shown in figure 4.1 for the cantilever beam. It will be seen that the shape of the first mode is smoother than any other, the shape of the second is smoother than the third and fourth and so on. For a given maximum amplitude of displacement the first mode will have a lower strain energy than the rest. Similarly mode two has a lower strain energy than modes three and four and so on with increasing mode number. So far as the kinetic energy is concerned every point on the beam, except for the built in end, is moving for the first mode and hence every point on the beam is contributing to the kinetic energy. For the second mode there are two points that are not moving and the mass at these points will not contribute to the kinetic energy for the mode. Similarly mode three has three positions along its length where it is stationary and the fourth mode has four points. For a

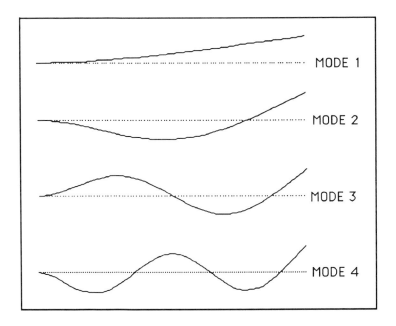

Fig 4.1 - Beam Mode Shapes

fixed maximum displacement amplitude for each mode there is more kinetic energy in the first mode than any other, more in the second mode than in the third or fourth and so on.

These results agree exactly with what is predicted by considerations of the Rayleigh quotient and explains why mode shapes become progressively more complicated in shape with increasing mode number. The only time that this simple argument does not apply is if the the structure consists of two or more dynamically independent components where different parts of the structure vibrate locally. In this case the modes of each component become progressively more complicated. It is worth noting, in passing, that if parts of the structure are dynamically isolated from each other then they can be modelled more efficiently as two separate structures.

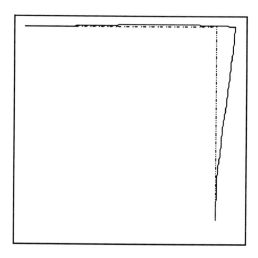

Fig 4.2 - Static Deflected Shape

## 4.4 Finite Element Modelling Implications of the Rayleigh Quotient.

For any form of dynamic response the displacement is largely controlled by the low modes of vibration. The velocity response is again controlled by the low modes but by rather more than those for the displacements. The general stress level tends to have the same convergence characteristics as the velocities. An accurate estimate of the accelerations requires many more modes to be considered. These general arguments can be used even when non-modal solution techniques are being used to provide, in conjunction with Rayleigh quotient considerations, arguments regarding the modelling requirements for a dynamic analysis. Generally the mesh should be such as to allow the kinetic energy to be maximised. It is not difficult to maximise a function. In simplistic terms it is just a process of adding all of the terms in the mass matrix together. This means that a very detailed description of the mass matrix is not required and a simple diagonal lumped mass model is often sufficient. A lumped mass model will always tend to slightly overestimate the effective dynamic mass so that mass lumping has the effect of reducing resonant frequencies. The finite element method tends to overestimate the stiffness which causes the resonant frequencies to be overestimated so that the two effects tend to cancel. This has been used as an argument in the past for choosing lumped mass models. However, while

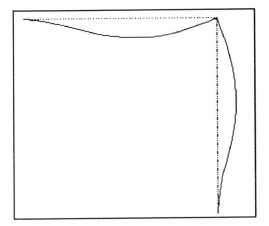

Fig 4.3 - First Mode Shape

lumping generally improves the resonant frequency estimates in a finite element element analysis it always causes a degradation in the calculated mode shapes and this leads to inaccuracies in the forced response. If only the lowest frequency response is of interest and the mesh is not very coarse then there is little difference between lumped and distributed mass solutions. Nodes should be located at positions of large mass. Often this is non-structural mass. As the required number of modes for the response increases then it becomes progressively more important to improve the mass idealisation of the structure. This is the case if there is a significant high frequency content in the forcing function, typically if the loading is impulsive as in impact problems, or if the loading is only located on a small part of the structure, typically a single point load at one node, or if the acceleration response is required. The more detailed mass idealisation can be achieved either by using a kinematically equivalent mass distribution or by having a finer mesh with a lumped mass idealisation.

The Rayleigh quotient implies that the strain energy has to be minimised for the low modes of vibration. This is a similar requirement to that for a static analysis so that, for dynamics, the stiffness has to be modelled to the same detail as is required to find displacements for a static problem. Dynamics pose one further major consideration over and above statics. For a static analysis some loading is applied and the finite element modelling only need be sufficient to find details of the response to the applied load. For a dynamic analysis, the lowest frequency mode shape will usually be excited most strongly and this can give rise to unexpected behaviour.

To illustrate this point consider the angle structures shown in Figures 4.2 and 4.3. For this the static load consists of an end pull at the end of the top horizontal member, giving the resulting deflected shape as shown, where there is little bending in the system. Most of the load is carried as end load in the top horizontal. A beam is a very efficient structural member when it is loaded in tension the cross-sectional area can be relatively small. However, consider now the first mode of vibration of the same structure, as shown in figure 4.3. It will be seen here that the deflection is all bending and there is no axial displacement of the top member. In terms of the Rayleigh quotient this arises because, for a given magnitude of deflection, there is very much less strain energy stored in thin beams when they are bending. For the example structure used in this illustration the first ten mode shapes were found and they were all bending modes with no axial extension. In practical terms this means that, if the structure is designed on purely static considerations for the given load then it is likely to have a very poor dynamic performance It also means that a mesh created for static analysis is likely to be unsuitable for dynamic purposes. Also, since the static behaviour has little bending the section properties, apart from the cross sectional area, need not be specified to a high accuracy. This is not the case for dynamics where, for the in-plane behaviour shown here, the second moments of area for the section are all important.

Incidentally, this illustration also shows the virtue of finding the resonant frequencies of a structure even when it is only being designed for a static load. The result presented here indicate that the structure will be very sensitive to any misapplication of the loading and might produce troubles in practice, even for statics.

Any operation on a matrix that implies minimising some function of it means that the matrix must be specified in considerable detail since the minimisation involves taking differences of terms in the matrix and this can give rise to numerical rounding errors. For the low modes of vibration the stiffness matrix has to be defined much more precisely than the mass matrix and cannot be specified to be diagonal as the mass matrix can.

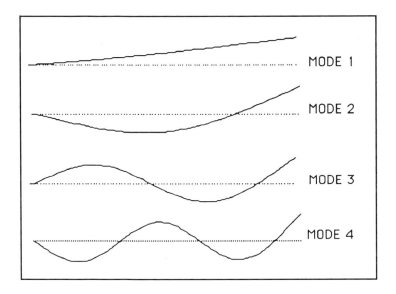

Fig 4.4 - Mode Shapes with Reduced Root Stiffness

The mesh should be chosen to allow the lowest stiffness areas of the structure to be modelled accurately. If the stiffness is distributed reasonably uniformly throughout the structure then a uniform mesh is required. If one area of the structure has a high stiffness then this area can be modelled with a coarse mesh. Alternatively, if part of the structure is flexible then it is likely that this should be modelled in some detail. One consequence of this is that the local flexibility of joints or other connectors can have a very significant effect upon the dynamic behaviour of the structure.

To illustrate this, consider the simple cantilever beam, with the mode shapes shown in figure 4.1. The beam model had twenty equal length elements. This was modified so that the first element only, at the root had, a Young's modulus of one half (and in a second test one tenth) that of the original. The resulting frequencies for the first ten modes are given in table 4.1. It will be seen that the lowest frequencies have been modified substantially but the higher frequencies show a relatively smaller change. This illustrates the sensitivity of the lowest frequencies to small stiffness changes. The first four mode shapes are shown in figure 4.4 for the case where the modulus of the first element was reduced by ten. It will be

| Mode | Resonant Frequencies (Hz) | | |
|------|----------|------|------|
| | Complete | E/2 | E/10 |
| 1 | 2.0 | 1.85 | 1.23 |
| 2 | 12.62 | 11.85 | 10.16 |
| 3 | 35.18 | 33.54 | 30.71 |
| 4 | 68.53 | 66.04 | 61.93 |
| 5 | 112.4 | 109.1 | 88.64 |
| 6 | 125.0 | 119.1 | 102.8 |
| 7 | 166.4 | 162.3 | 151.7 |
| 8 | 229.9 | 224.8 | 207.6 |
| 9 | 302.5 | 296.1 | 271.0 |
| 10 | 383.5 | 375.4 | 343.2 |

Table 4.1 - Resonant Frequencies of the Modified Cantilever

seen that there is relatively little change in the mode shapes when compared to figure 4.1. The most noticeable changes are at the root, as is to be expected, but the general shapes of the modes are the same.

## 4.5 Finite Element Modelling Considerations

As with a static analysis, the choice of element type depends upon the problem that is to be solved and what is required from the analysis. If it is only necessary to find the resonant frequencies then a relatively coarse mesh of simple elements is required. Thin walled structures such as beams and plates are always prone to vibration with relatively low natural frequencies. In such cases the structure can be modelled using beam and plate elements. These models, based upon the centre line geometry of the structure, means that the precise details of connections are not well defined. Provided that the connection is relatively stiff then this detail tends not to affect the low frequency modes and it is not necessary to include the detail. However, there are some connection details that must be included. If plates are reinforced by off-set stiffeners then the off-set must be included in the model.

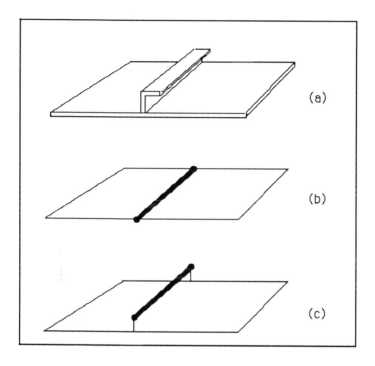

Fig 4.5 - Modelling of Stiffened Plates

This is illustrated in figure 4.5. The actual plate with a typical reinforcing stiffener is shown in figure 4.5a. If the plate is modelled as plate elements and the stiffener section is modelled as a beam then a direct assembly of the elements will produce the model shown in figure 4.5b. This does not include the fact that the principal axis of the beam is offset from the centre line of the plate. In this case the effective stiffness of the reinforcing member will be considerably under estimated since it can only undergo pure bending in sympathy with the plate bending. If figure 4.5c the stiffener is modelled with rigid offsets (or multi-point constraints) so that the neutral axis of the beam is in the correct position relative to the centre line of the plate. A bending action of the plate will now induce a membrane stretching of the stiffener and the whole structure will be considerably stiffer and have higher frequencies than the model of figure 4.5b. The importance of this detail depends

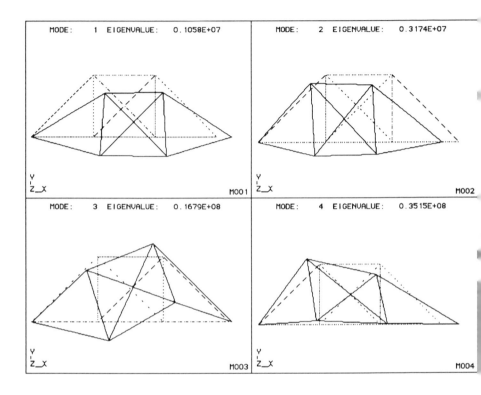

Fig 4.6 - Mode Shapes of a Pin Jointed Frame Work

upon the relative size and stiffness of the stiffener in relation to the plate. It also depends upon the the nature of the full structure geometry and the vibration response that is being considered. If the complete structure is a flat plate with a series of these stiffeners then this detail of modelling is important. Likewise, it is important if the local plate vibration modes of a built up structure are being considered. However, it is probably not important if the overall modes of the complete structure are of interest. Typically, this type of reinforcing is found on the skins of aircraft structures. If the modes of vibration of the complete aircraft are of interest and local panel bending is not being considered then the modelling of figure 4.5b will be sufficient. Here only the cross-sectional area of the beam is specified since the local bending can be ignored.

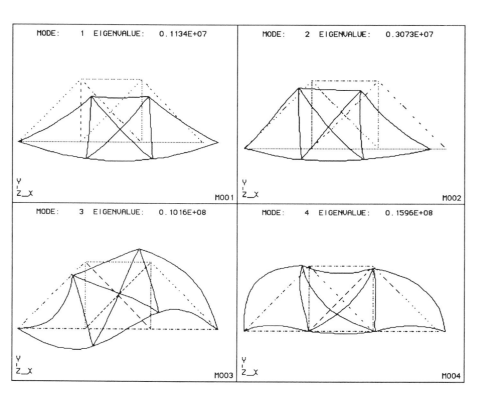

Fig 4.7 - Mode Shapes of a Rigid Jointed Frame Work

To illustrate this a framework structure has been analysed as a pin jointed and rigid jointed. The first four modes of vibration for each model are shown in figure 4.6 for the pin jointed model and figure 4.7 for the rigid jointed one. The resonant frequencies for the first four modes of the two models are given in table 4.2. It will be seen that there is a reasonably close agreement between the first two resonant frequencies. The mode shapes are also generally the same, given that the bars in the pinned model are assumed to stay straight but they can bend in the rigid jointed model. One point of interest is that there is no consistency as to which model produces the lowest frequency estimate, mode one of the pinned structure is lower than mode one of the rigid joint model  but mode two is higher. This is because two different approximations are involved and they have a different significance

| Mode | Resonant Frequencies (Hz) | |
|---|---|---|
| | Pinned | Rigid |
| 1 | 163.7 | 169.5 |
| 2 | 283.6 | 279.0 |
| 3 | 652.2 | 507.3 |
| 4 | 943.6 | 635.9 |

Table 4.2 - Resonant Frequencies of the Framework Models

for different modes. In the pinned model the joints have no rotational stiffness, which is an underestimate of the true stiffness, but the bars are assumed to stay straight, which is an overestimate. For the rigid jointed model the assumption of rigid joints will overestimate the joint stiffness but the bending flexibility of the bars is included in this model. As a consequence of these combined assumptions no single trend emerges between the results. However, the fact that both models, with very different assumptions, give very similar values for the first two frequencies provides a level of confidence that the results are likely to agree with reality.

There is a much wider disagreement between the next two resonant frequencies. Looking at the mode shapes for mode three of the two models, it will be seen that they are both modes involving rotation of the centre bay and are the same mode. Allowing the beams to bend provides considerably more flexibility than pinning the joints hence the rigid jointed model has the lower frequency. It is just about possible to identify the fourth mode shape as being the same between the two models but there is a very large difference in the resonant frequencies. Again, the fact that the members can flex locally is more important than the nature of the joints.This is generally the case and it follows from considerations of the Rayleigh quotient. As higher modes are considered so the mode shapes become more complicated and the idealisation that allows more overall movement tends to give better results. In other words, to calculate the higher modes the elements should allow more local deflection (for example allow bending as in this case) combined with the fact that the mesh needs to be finer. The finer the mesh the more the local detail of any mode can be defined. Another result of this comparison which, seems to apply in general, is that the effect of the fine details of joints and supports is increasingly less important with increasing mode number. To obtain the first resonant frequency accurately the nature of the supports, joints and interconnections needs to be defined reasonably precisely but for the higher modes it is the fineness of the mesh and the freedoms allowed within the element shape functions that are important.

## 4.6 Choice of Element Type

The choice of element type is very much conditioned by the problem that is to be solved. In many cases the considerations in choosing the element are identical to those for a static analysis, such considerations being:

1. What elements are available in the system
2. Which elements have past experience shown to be accurate and economical for the type of problem under consideration.
3. What elements are recommended for use.
4. Is the behaviour three dimensional or can it be considered to be two dimensional. If so is it in the plane or normal to the plane of the structure.
5. If a forced response is to be conducted does the element have suitable kinematically equivalent loads.
6. If more than one element is required are the elements compatible. This can be even more important for a dynamic analysis since the incompatibilities between the element types can lead to considerable under or over estimates of strain energy and can affect the low frequency response considerably.

Other considerations specific to the dynamic analysis must also be made. As discussed in the previous section the low frequency behaviour can be modelled in terms of how the static model is derived but, as higher frequencies are considered then the local behaviour of the structure becomes more important. Because of this it is likely that a membrane model, such as the pin jointed framework in the previous section, becomes less reliable and both bending and membrane behaviour must be included in the model. If there is any doubt it is better to err on the side of caution and include bending effects but a price will be paid for this in terms of increased computer resource requirements. If bending elements are used then the degrees of freedom are both displacements and rotations and these have different units. Because they have different units then the relative size of terms in the stiffness matrix become a function of the unit of length used for the analysis. This is not the case for two or three dimensional solid elements where the relative size of terms in the stiffness matrix is independent of the units of length. These different units mean that, for bending elements, the condition number (which defines the likely numerical stability of the analysis) is a function of the units used for the analysis. In such a case the analyst should choose the length units to be comparable with the size of the structure, that is, if the structure is some metres long using metres as the basic unit of length is less likely to cause numerical difficulties than using millimetres. If there is no numerical problems then running the analysis with either set of units gives the same solution. This problem of units for a bending analysis has been found to be particularly severe when the structure can undergo rigid body motions.

As with a static analysis, if there is any uncertainty about the form of response or the best element types to use, one or more simple parametric studies should be undertaken before the full analysis is carried out. These consist of very simplified models of the problem, or some parts of the problem, that allow the user to gain a feel for the analysis, to anticipate what the results will be and to assess the effects of the change of any parameter defining the structure. Such studies are extremely useful in dynamics since it can be difficult to use intuition to say what the response will be like. They have also proved useful on occasions for showing that the low frequency response could be modelled using a much simpler mesh than was initially though to be required.

In choosing the element type some consideration should also be given to the mass matrix of the element. As discussed in section 4.3 it is usually possible to use a very coarse lumped mass idealisation and some systems only generate lumped mass elements. These can begin to be deficient for the higher frequency or transient response models and are compensated for by using a finer mesh. If only the mode shape or displacement response is required then a lumped mass model is almost always sufficient. If velocity or acceleration response is required then it might be worth while conducting some pilot studies comparing between lumped and kinematically equivalent mass models to assess their relative accuracy and efficiency.

Thin structures are more prone to vibration than solid ones hence many dynamic analyses can often be conducted using beam and/or plate elements. If only the low frequency response is being considered it is likely that relatively thick solid structures that would be modelled statically using brick elements can be modelled for a dynamic analysis by means of thick shell elements. One situation where this would not apply is associated with impact or impulsively loaded structures. Here waves can propagate within the material and, if most of then energy is in terms of this internal wave propagation, then a three dimensional model (or a two dimensional slice if applicable) will be required.

For a static analysis the choice of element interpolation order is usually either second order, (eight node quadrilaterals and twenty node bricks) or in some specially developed high performance first order elements. The main advantage of the second order elements lie in the fact that they can be used with reduced integration which means that they are computationally efficient.They also allow curved geometries to be modelled more accurately The analyst should check that reduced integration can be used for dynamic problems since there is a theoretical possibility of having spurious zero strain energy modes. These appear as zero eigenvalue modes in a dynamic analysis and could cause numerical difficulties in the solution process. Generally, provided that the same rules are followed as in a static analysis to prevent the zero energy modes from propagating, then their dynamic performance is good. One possible problem that might be encountered with reduced integration elements is in association with unsupported structures. In this case the complete structure has zero frequency rigid body modes associated with it and the assembled stiffness matrix is singular. These rigid body modes present difficulties to some eigenvalue extraction techniques and the numerical problems can be exacerbated in some cases by reduced integration, even when the rule is completely acceptable statically. In other cases special constraint modes are added to the element formulation to constrain the rigid body modes. These constraint modes can also provide difficulty for dynamic problems since, if the constraint is not high enough it will not prevent the singular behaviour for the higher frequencies. Alternatively, if the constraint is too high it can give rise to numerical problems for eigenvalue extraction and require very short time steps for some step-by-step integration solution methods.

## 4.7 Choice of Mesh

In a static analysis the element mesh density is usually greatest around areas of stress concentration. If stresses are to be found as a part of the dynamic response calculation then the same considerations apply as for dynamics. However, if only the frequencies and mode shapes or the just the displacements, velocities or accelerations are required from a forced response then stress concentrations are not relevant. This can be concluded from the Rayleigh quotient since the mode shapes of the lowest modes (that is those that are dynamically most important) are defined by the displacement shapes that minimise the strain energy and maximise the kinetic energy. A stress concentration does exactly the reverse of this. A confined local variation in the displacements in the local region of the stress concentration gives rise to a large increase in the strain energy but, since these displacements are local, they will have little effect upon the kinetic energy. In other words, the lowest modes of vibration will tend not to excite stress concentrations. There is therefore no reason to design a mesh to give an accurate estimate of the stress concentration if it is not significant in the response.

The best strategy for a dynamic mesh is the simplest one of having a uniform mesh over the structure. It can be coarser in the stiff parts of the structure and finer in the flexible parts or where heavy masses are located. Since, for any linear response and for a large number of non-linear dynamic problems, the response is a linear combination of the modes of vibration the mesh should be suitable for describing the deformed shape given by each mode. Almost invariably this will involve a significant response amplitude of all points on the structure, hence the argument that a uniform mesh is to be preferred. If stresses are required and there are areas of stress concentration then an increased mesh density should be used in these areas. Methods for recovering the stresses are discussed in Chapter 8.

If there there are significant structural or non-structural masses located at some points in the structure then the user should try to ensure that nodes are located at the centre of gravity of these masses in order to maximise that the kinetic energy as accurately as possible. For non-structural masses their centre of gravity often occurs at positions offset from the structure. In such cases rigid offsets or multi-point constraints should be used to  locate nodes at the centre of gravity of the mass. One of the problems associated with non-structural masses is that  they vary in magnitude as the structure is used. Typically, the

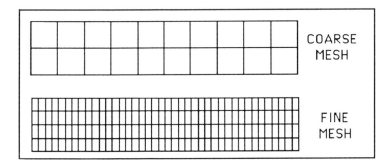

Fig 4.8 - Meshes for Frequency Comparisons

payload on a transport aircraft is of the same order as the structural weight and can therefore affect the resonant frequencies. However, this changes from flight to flight and, in the case of the fuel, during the flight. Similarly in the winter the roof of a building can carry a weight of snow that is greater than the roof weight. Normally assuming the maximum value for the non-structural mass is most conservative since this will give the lowest resonant frequencies. However, if the structure is subjected to steady state periodic loading then the two extremes of maximum non-structural mass and minimum non-structural mass should be investigated to ensure that, over the operating range, there is not any coincidence between a resonant frequency and an excitation frequency.

If the stiffness distribution of the structure is not uniform then the mesh density should be greater in the areas of low stiffness since this will allow the strain energy to be minimised. If a part of the structure is much stiffer than the rest then the analyst should model this as being rigid. This can be conveniently done in most systems by means of lumped masses and multi-point constraint equations. If the stiffness is very low in some regions of the structure attention must be paid to these areas at the modelling stage. If the stiffness is very low it can be modelled as zero stiffness or as pinned joints. In more complicated situations a refined mesh is required to define the stiffness in sufficient detail. Such considerations are relatively less important if the areas of low stiffness are not primary load carrying paths for the structure but they become very important if all of the loading passes through a low stiffness region. One typical structural area where this occurs is at structural joints.

| FREQUENCIES (HZ) | | |
| MODE  COARSE MESH | FINE MESH | % DIFFERENCE |
| --- | --- | --- |
| 4     93.15 | 93.10 | 0.05 |
| 5     218.8 | 218.4 | 0.18 |
| 6     255.0 | 255.0 | 0.00 |
| 7     366.0 | 364.3 | 0.46 |
| 8     507.3 | 507.2 | 0.02 |
| 9     518.8 | 514.3 | 0.87 |
| 10    670.4 | 661.1 | 1.39 |
| 11    751.6 | 751.0 | 0.08 |
| 12    786.4 | 776.4 | 1.27 |
| 13    873.2 | 862.0 | 1.24 |
| 14    888.8 | 876.5 | 1.38 |
| 15    971.5 | 968.6 | 2.99 |
| 16    1031. | 1012. | 1.84 |
| 17    1050. | 1022. | 2.67 |
| 18    1131. | 1124. | 0.62 |

Table 4.3 - Frequency Differences Between Fine and Coarse Meshes

To illustrate the effect of mesh density on resonant frequencies an unsupported two dimensional deep beam structure was analysed with two different mesh densities. The two meshes used are shown in figure 4.8. The fine mesh had more than double the mesh density of the coarse mesh. The resonant frequencies of the two meshes are compared in table 3. It will be seen that for the first eighteen modes of vibration (the first three zero frequency rigid body modes are not included in the table) there is a very close agreement between the two sets of resonant frequencies. The trend is for the difference between the two sets of frequencies to increase with mode number. This trend is not monotonic since the mode shapes for the structure are of two types, axial stretching or bending. The increase in percentage frequency difference then tends to follow the two categories of mode shapes, with the axial modes agreeing best in this case

### 4.7.1 Wave Propagation Meshes

One problem type that requires special consideration for the mesh used is the case where waves can be propagated through the structure. This occurs for impact type problems and in seismic soil-structure interaction problems where the seismic wave can propagate through the foundation material. A finite element model is quite capable of representing the propagation of waves provided that the correct mesh is used. A finite element is only an approximation to real life in that it has been restricted to a finite number of degrees of freedom. This has the implication that a given element can only propagate waves accurately up to a cut off frequency defined by the size of the element and its shape functions. The element acts as a low pass filter and will filter out the high frequency components of the signal.

The precise cut off frequency for an element should be found from pilot studies but, as a rule of thumb, the length between nine consecutive nodes can be taken as the shortest wavelength that can be propagated. Knowing the wave speed this can then be used to estimate approximately the highest frequency that the mesh can propagate accurately. With wave propagation problems the wave front will travel through all points in the structure, given sufficient time. This means that all points within the mesh are equally important at different times in the response and therefore a uniform mesh is required. If a non-uniform mesh is used the finer part of the mesh will propagate higher frequencies than the coarser part. There will then be reflections of the high frequency components in the wave at the boundaries between the fine and the coarse meshes and the waves will not propagate correctly. The mesh must be fine enough in its coarsest region for it to propagate the highest frequency in the input. If this condition is not met then the response will be under estimated, the coarser the mesh the greater the under estimate. A finer mesh can be used in areas where stresses are required, provided that the coarsest region of the mesh is sufficiently fine to propagate the frequencies in the input. If stresses are not being computed then a uniform mesh can be used.

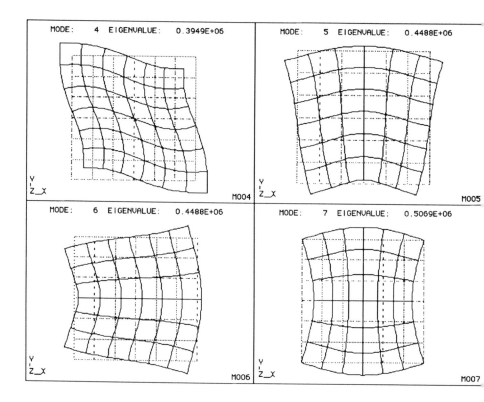

<u>Fig 4.9 - Modes of a Plate with Quarter Symmetry</u>

## 4.8  Use of Symmetry

If the structure has one or more planes of symmetry then this can be used to reduce the cost of a dynamic analysis.If only the resonant frequencies and mode shapes are required then the use of symmetry presents no problems. It can be shown that the eigenvectors of the structure will also have the same symmetries. The eigenvalue problem can be solved as a series of smaller problems. If the structure has one plane of symmetry then the modes can be found by generating the geometry for half of the structure and two runs made, one with symmetric boundary conditions and one with antisymmetry. If the geometry has a quarter symmetry four separate eigenvalue problems are solved, with boundary conditions of (1) symmetry/symmetry, (2) symmetry/antisymmetry, (3) antisymmetry/symmetry and (4) antisymmetry/antisymmetry. In some cases (2) and (3) give identical structures and will have the same frequencies. The mode shapes are also the same but rotated by ninety degrees. In this case only three small problems need be solved.

It is always computationally cheaper to solve a series of small problems rather than one big one, and this is especially the case for the eigenvalue problem. It is also advantageous to use symmetry from the point of numerical stability. Some eigenvalue extraction methods have difficulty with multiple eigenvalues. Structures with geometrical symmetry are much more likely to have multiple eigenvalues than arbitrary geometries. Further multiple roots tend to be associated with different symmetries, typically the modes for symmetric/antisymmetric boundary conditions are often identical to those for antisymmetry/symmetry boundary conditions. This possible difficulty is removed if symmetry is used.

Figure 4.9 shows the first four non-zero in plane modes for a free/free square plate. It will be seen from this that mode 4 is an antisymmetric/antisymmetric mode. Modes 5 and 6 are symmetric/antisymmetric modes. They have identical eigenvalues and their mode shapes are the same but rotated by ninety degrees. Mode 7 is a symmetric/symmetric mode. Symmetry conditions were not used to compute these mode shapes. Identical modes and frequencies would have been found more efficiently if symmetry had been used.

### 4.8.1 Axial Symmetry

Many structures are rotationally symmetric in the form of cylinders or spheres, since such shapes are easy to form and are efficient for carrying pressure loads. Some finite element systems have elements that exploit such axial symmetries, where only the cross section of the structure need be defined by the user and the element formulation rotates this about the axis of symmetry. For most mechanical loadings the loads are constant around the circumference and it is assumed that the displacements are also constant around the circumference. However, this is only the first term in a more general Fourier series where the displacements can vary around the circumference in the form

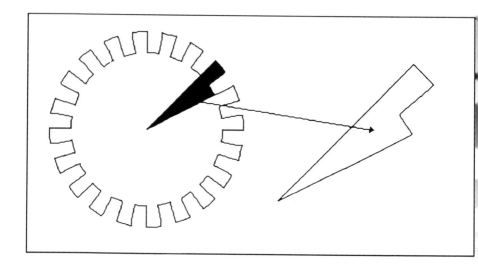

<u>Fig 4.10 - Structure with Cyclic Symmetry</u>

$r = \Sigma\, r_{cn}\, \cos(n\theta) + \Sigma\, r_{sn}\, \sin(n\theta)$

where $\theta$ is the angle around the circumference, $r_{cn}$ are the amplitudes of the cosine components and $r_{sn}$ are the amplitudes of the sine components in the Fourier series. It is possible to choose a combination of these sine and cosine components such that there is a separate eigenvalue problem for each harmonic, n, in the Fourier series. This gives a very efficient method for calculating the resonant frequencies of axisymmetric structures. It is usually found that the lowest resonant frequency occurs in the range of n=2 to 5.

### 4.8.2 Cyclic Symmetry

Some structures are rotationally symmetric whilst not being axially symmetric. A typical structure of this type is a gas turbine disc with the blades attached. The complete geometry can be constructed by replicating and rotating the sector containing a single blade. It is possible to utilise this cyclic symmetry in a manner similar to, but more complicated than, the Fourier series used in the case of axial symmetry. Appropriate combinations of boundary conditions can be applied to each of the faces of the sector and again the eigenvalue problem can be decomposed into a series of small problems of the size of a single sector. The application of these boundary conditions is not straightforward and requires the finite element system to have the appropriate coding available. Where it is available and applicable then cyclic symmetry should always be used since it can give orders of magnitude reduction in the cost of the eigenvalue extraction if there are many sectors that are repeated.

Figure 4.10 shows a structure with cyclic symmetry. In this case the dynamics of the complete structure can be found by analysing just the shaded sector, provided that the finite element analysis system being used has a cyclic symmetry facility.

### 4.8.3 Problems with the use of Symmetry

If only the eigenvalues and eigenvectors are required then there are no problems associated with any of the forms of symmetry. They always lead to a reduction in the analysis cost and generally improve the numerical conditioning of the eigenvalue problem and should be used.

If a forced response is required or a non-modal solution method is being used then the use of symmetry can become cumbersome, depending upon the exact nature of the loading and the facilities available within the finite element system. If the loading can be defined in terms of one of the symmetries then there are no difficulties since only this one set of boundary conditions need be considered. However, if the loading is general then it has to be decomposed into the various symmetries and each one solved separately. The resulting responses for each boundary condition have to be recombined to give the total response. This has to be repeated at each time step or frequency point. If the system contains facilities to automatically decompose the general loading and for recombining the various responses into the total response then symmetry should be used. If it does not have these facilities the solution process ceases to be feasible in most cases, purely from the data handling point of view, and the choice of whether or not to utilise symmetries in the geometry must be considered carefully for the general forced response.

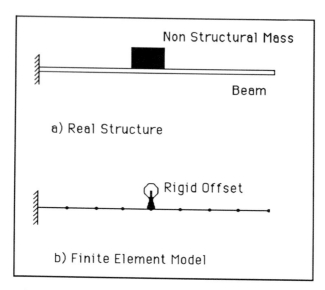

Fig 4.11 - Modelling non-Structural Mass with Constraints

## 4.9 Multi-point Constraints

As with static modelling multi-point constraints can be very useful for dynamic modelling. This goes under various names in different systems and sometimes called constraint equations, generalised constraints, rigid offsets or rigid stalks. The use of such constraints has already been mentioned in section 4.5 where they were used to model the offset between the centre surface of a plate and the principal axis of a beam. This is typical of the use of constraint equations within the modelling process. Constraint equations can also be used to force lines to be straight but still allow them to move. An example of this is to treat a thick concrete slab that supports a building and which itself sits on a flexible soil foundation, as a rigid slab. Constraint equations can be devised to allow the slab to translate and rotate as a rigid body but to stop it having any elastic movements. Numerically this is much better than the alternative of modelling the slab in terms of finite elements and assigning a high stiffness to the elements in the slab since this almost invariably leads to an ill conditioned set of equations.

Constraint equations can be used whenever a part of the structure has a very high stiffness. The constraints allow the limit of an infinite stiffness to be assumed. One important use of constraint equations within dynamics is to allow the centre of gravity of non-structural masses to be correctly positioned. This is done by putting a rigid connection between the centre of gravity of the mass and the nearest node point. This is illustrated in figure 4.11

Here the large rigid mass is modelled using constraint equations to position its centre of gravity correctly with respect to the principal axis of the beam. The fact the the centre of gravity is offset means that it has a relatively high rotational inertia and this will lower the resonant frequencies which in turn will tend to increase the response amplitude.

*4.9.1 Problems with Constraint Equations*

There can be some problems associated with the use of constraint equations. The nature of these depend, to some extent, upon the manner in which constraint equations have been implemented within the finite element system. If more than one structural node is involved in defining the constraint equations (a multi-point constraint rather than a single point constraint ) then the constraint equations can easily upset the band width of the equations and make the solution computationally expensive. It is best to number the constraint nodes to be grouped together if possible to reduce the effect of the change of band width of the equations. This can be difficult with those programs that renumber the equations automatically internally within the program. If two nodes that span a large topological distance across the structure are connected with constraint equations then, inevitably, the band width of the equation set will be increased considerably.

Care must also be taken in using any form of constraint equations with a lumped or diagonalised mass matrix formulation. In the example in figure 4.11 the offset of the mass from the centre line of the beam appears as off-diagonal terms in the mass matrix. If the mass matrix is then forced to be diagonal before solution or eigenvalue extraction then a significant part of the offset mass effect can be lost and the wrong answers will be obtained. This effect is more pronounced the larger the mass and the greater the offset. If the constraints are being used to model the positions of the centre of gravity of rigid masses then diagonal mass matrices should be avoided.

One other practical problem associated with constraint equations is the difficulty associated with checking that the constraints have been correctly applied. Nodes that have been tied together with constraints can be displayed graphically but it is difficult to display the nature of the constraint. The more complicated the constraints sets are then the more difficult it is to check that they have been applied as required. The user should inspect the calculated response or the computed mode shapes very carefully to confirm that the constraint equations have been applied correctly. This is not an easy task.

## 4.10  Cost and Accuracy

It is very difficult to give any general guidelines between cost and accuracy for dynamic problems since it is so dependent upon the nature of the problem being solved. If the same mesh is being used for both static and dynamic analysis then the computational cost of the dynamic analysis will be significantly higher than the cost of the static analysis. This is because the dynamic analysis can be considered as repeated applications of the same set of operations that are used in statics and hence the greater cost. A dynamic analysis will also produce a much greater volume of output than a static one so that the time required to review the results will be correspondingly greater.

In many cases, especially where either just the lowest natural frequencies or the displacement response for relatively low frequencies are required, then the computational cost of the dynamic analysis can be reduced considerably by building a separate dynamic model. Generally this can have a much coarser mesh than the one required for statics and often simpler elements can be used. Typically beams and plates can be used for dynamic models where solid elements would be required for a static analysis. The simpler model means a reduction in man time in investigating and verifying the results.

In general terms the accuracy of the dynamic solution follows the same trends as a static analysis with regard to the finite element approximation. For the same number of elements second order shape functions are more accurate than first order ones. In practice it has been found that lumped mass models are almost always used in preference to the kinematically equivalent mass with no noticeable reduction in the accuracy of the solution but with a significant reduction in its cost.

# CHAPTER 5 - PROBLEM REDUCTION

## 5.1 Introduction

Any dynamic analysis is inevitably more expensive than a static analysis since its solution involves repeated computations of the same form as a single computation for a static analysis. This leads to the question being asked 'Can the cost of the dynamic computation be reduced?'. The answer to this is inevitably yes but a subsidiary question must also be asked, namely 'Can the cost of the dynamic computation be reduced without significantly affecting the accuracy of the results?'. It is much more difficult to answer this question since an assessment must now be made of what loss of accuracy is associated with the cost reduction process. There are a variety of techniques for reducing the cost of a dynamic analysis, the problem lies in quantifying the consequences of the reduction analysis. Within the literature the term condensation is often used as a synonym for reduction. The terms dynamic reduction and dynamic condensation mean exactly the same and both will be used here.

All of the problem reduction techniques aim to reduce the cost of the analysis by decreasing the number of degrees of freedom used in the analysis. The fundamental assumption is that the low frequency modes of vibration are those that are important and the higher the mode then the less important it is in the dynamic analysis. It is certainly true that, for any numerical model, and especially for a finite element model, the high frequency modes are less accurate when compared to differential equation solutions. However, it is not always correct to infer that this means that they are progressively less important. The purpose of the dynamic analysis and the results that are required must be defined before this inference can be made. If only the resonant frequencies or the displacement response is required then only the low modes are important and a considerable reduction in the number of degrees of freedom can be made without a significant loss of accuracy. If the velocity response is required then it can be shown that more degrees of freedom must be included in the model than the number required for just the displacement analysis. Similarly, progressively more degrees of freedom are required for an accurate estimation of the acceleration. It is more difficult to relate the number of modes required for an accurate estimations of stress to the number required for a displacement analysis. If there are no significant stress concentrations within the structure then the accuracy of the stress results is about the same as the accuracy of the velocity response. However, if there is a strong stress concentration then considerably more degrees of freedom are required.

The form of forcing function is also important when deciding upon the required complexity of the dynamic model. If an harmonic forcing function is applied and the steady state response is required then the maximum response occurs if the forcing function has a frequency component close to a resonant frequency. In this case it is necessary that the finite element model must be sufficiently accurate to represent the resonant frequencies over the range of frequencies within the forcing function so that no significant resonant frequencies are missed. If the forcing function is not periodic then there is not a simple relationship between the the structural resonant frequencies and the frequency content of the forcing function. However, there is still an effective frequency defined within the forcing function given by how rapidly the forcing function changes from one state to another, that is the rise time of the input. If the force changes rapidly it has a short rise time and the input has a high frequency content. A relatively large number of degrees of freedom are then required in the model. If the force input only changes relatively slowly, that is it has a long rise time, then it has a lower frequency content and fewer modes are required in the analysis.

The number of degrees of freedom in a model is basically controlled by the number of nodes in the mesh. If the dynamic model is being constructed from scratch the mesh used can reflect the required results. At one extreme, if only the first few resonant frequencies or if only the displacement response is required, then a coarse mesh can be used. Often this mesh is much coarser than that used for an equivalent static stress analysis. However, if the dynamic stresses are required then a mesh density commensurate with that used for static stressing is needed. In this case the mesh can be graduated in the regions of stress concentrations exactly as for a static stress analysis. The most computationally expensive dynamic model arises for impact and wave propagation problems. Here the rise times of the forcing function is short requiring a relatively large number of degrees of freedom. In addition there will be large changes in stresses and displacements at the front of the wave so that a fine mesh is required to model the wave front accurately. However, the wave front moves through the complete model as the wave propagates so that a uniformly fine mesh is required throughout the model for wave propagation problems.

Very often the dynamic model is not created from scratch. Instead, a static model exists that has been designed and used for stress analysis purposes. Since the cost of building a finite element model of any real structure is relatively expensive it makes considerable sense to utilise any existing model for a dynamic analysis where this is possible. There are various methods of automatically condensing static models to smaller dynamic models but, for the various reasons outlined above, these must be used with care since they are only applicable in certain cases depending upon what is required within the response. For some cases, typically when calculating dynamic stresses, then the degree of condensation depends partly upon the reduction process used and also upon how the stresses are to be recovered after the displacements have been found. These two points must be considered together when deciding upon the degree of condensation employed within the analysis. If an impulse or wave propagation problem is being solved then a uniform mesh density is required. In such cases it is very likely that the static model will not be sufficiently detailed for correctly predicting the propagation response and, almost invariably, a separate more detailed dynamic model is required. This is not a condensation process and a new model must be built.

## 5.2  Reduction Methods

All dynamic reduction methods are approximate and, because different approximations can be used, there is a great range of forms of dynamic reduction. All of these different forms have their own sub variants. The main classification of dynamic reduction techniques are:

*   Modal Reduction - where only a small number of the possible modes of vibration are used for the forced response calculation.
*   Static Condensation - where the method of reducing the effective number of degrees of freedom is based entirely upon static considerations

• Dynamic Condensation - where the method of reducing the effective number of degrees of freedom is based upon both static and dynamic considerations.

• Dynamic Substructuring - where the complete structure is formed by establishing a reduced set of equations for a set of components, or substructures, that compose the total structure.

All reduction (or condensation) techniques are based upon the same principle. The aim is to reduce the effective number of degrees of freedom and so reduce computational costs. All four methods can be written in terms of a coordinate transformation of the form

$$r = Tq$$

Where r is the full set of displacements of size (nx1), q is the reduced or condensed set of displacements of size (mx1) where m<n and T is a transformation matrix relating the two sets of coordinates together. The various reduction techniques can then be looked upon as different methods for constructing a suitable transformation matrix.

There are very many possible ways of defining the transformation matrix T but not all are equally accurate for a dynamic analysis. Various points can be considered that should be satisfied and most methods of condensing the equations form some compromise between the requirements. The most important point is that the dynamic behaviour is largely controlled by the lowest modes of vibration and that that any condensation method should allow the lower modes to be recovered with a smaller error than the higher ones. Secondly, the higher modes of vibration will still contribute to the dynamic response but if the maximum frequency content of the forcing function is significantly lower than a particular resonant frequency then the contribution of that high resonance to the overall response will be in terms of a constant (static) value. This is illustrated in figure 5.1. Before the frequency $\omega$, mode 2 has a substantially constant response and its contribution to the overall response is defined almost entirely by its stiffness over this range. This is not the case for mode 1 which varies considerably over the frequency range 0 to $\omega$ and the dynamic behaviour of this mode is required. If a frequency of $2\omega$ or higher is of interest then the second mode must also be modelled dynamically. In general the transformation matrix T must be constructed to allow the low frequency modes to be defined by their dynamic response and the high frequency modes to be defined by their static response.

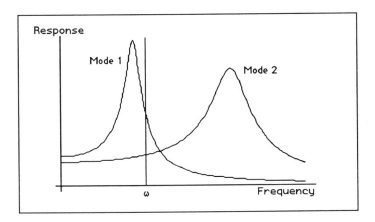

Fig 5.1 - Individual Modal Response

Once a transformation has been defined then the equation of motion

$$M\ddot{r} + C\dot{r} + Kr = R$$

can be condensed from the full set of n equations to the small set m by means of the transformation matrix $T$. The condensed equations are

$$M_c\ddot{q} + C_c\dot{q} + K_cq = Q$$

where

$$M_c = T^tMT \quad ; \quad C_c = T^tCT \quad ; \quad K_c = T^tKT \quad ; \quad Q = T^tR$$

with $M_c$, $C_c$ and $K_c$ all being (mxm) symmetric matrices. $Q$ is the (mx1) reduced load vector and $q$ the (mx1) reduced displacement vector. For any of the condensation methods this represents the equation set that is to be solved. For a dynamic substructuring analysis these are the equations for a component and are subsequently assembled together with other components.

## 5.3 Accuracy of Reduction Methods

For a static analysis it can be shown that a solution by means of substructuring is exact. If the full structure is analysed directly and then analysed as a series of substructures it is found that, apart from round off error, the two solutions are identical. There is no approximation involved in static substructuring. This is not the case with dynamic substructures. When the equations of any individual substructure are reduced in size then information regarding the dynamic response, that is information regarding the higher resonant frequencies and mode shapes, is lost. The solution can be arranged to preserve the stiffness characteristics associated with the high frequency modes but not the mass characteristics. Thus a static substructure solution is exact but a dynamic substructure solution is only approximate. The only time that the dynamic substructure solution is exact is if the equations are solved in the frequency domain at a specific frequency $\omega$ so that a set of dynamic stiffness equations of the form

$$(\mathbf{K}+i\omega\mathbf{C} - \omega^2\mathbf{M}) \sin(\omega t) = \mathbf{G} \sin(\omega t)$$

is solved. This is identical in form to a static solution with complex coefficients and so it is exact. However, the method is restricted to solving single frequency response. It becomes very expensive if a range of frequencies have to be considered since the equations have to be reformulated for each separate frequency.

## 5.4 Modal Reduction

Modal reduction is carried out automatically when only a reduced set of modes are used in the response calculation. In this case each column in the transformation matrix, $\mathbf{T}$, is an eigenvector of the system. The transformation to the reduced set of equations has the added advantage that the reduced stiffness and mass matrices are both diagonal. For the assumption of either proportional damping or modal damping then the reduced damping matrix is also diagonal. This is exploited in solving the forced response of the equations since the reduced equations are a set of m uncoupled single degree of freedom equations.

In modal reduction the contribution of all of the modes that are included in the transformation is found exactly. The response, however, is not exact even for a low frequency input since the static contributions of the high frequency modes have not been included. This is not important if the excitation is near one of the low resonant frequencies since the response of this mode will then dominate. Away from any resonance it can lead to a significant error. The major drawback to modal condensation is that the first m eigenvectors of the full (nxn) system must be found before it can be employed. In practice it is the calculation of these eigenvectors that is expensive and so modal condensation only reduces the cost marginally. This is not the case if some of the specialised, sparse matrix eigenvalue extraction techniques such as subspace iteration or the Lanczos method are used since these are designed to find only the first m eigenvectors.

The usual assumptions for damping is that it is either proportional or modal and the reduction of the damping matrix does not introduce any errors or approximations other than those discussed for the undamped system. If a more detailed model of the damping is included in the form of a specific damping matrix which is not proportional damping then the reduction process can lead to significant errors. In developing the equations for the response of structures with non-proportional damping it is found that the displacement and velocity response must each be found as separate, unrelated quantities. However, they are obviously related since the velocity is the time derivative of the displacement. Detailed investigation reveals that this relationship is only satisfied if the transformation matrix used in condensing the equations with arbitrary damping is a square non-singular matrix. In order to achieve this the modal condensation of an arbitrarily damped system is carried out in two stages. Initially the damping is considered as zero and the first m undamped eigenvectors found and these are used to condense the equations. The reduced equations are no longer diagonal, or rather the reduced damping matrix is not, but then all of the damped eigenvectors of the condensed equations are found and these are used derive the uncoupled equations. In practice very few finite element systems allow the definition of arbitrary damping matrices and most only have some form of modal or proportional damping representation so that this does not present a practical problem.

Modal condensation is normally used as an integral part of finding the modal response. It can, however, also be used to condense the equations for a step-by-step type of solution method or even for non-linear response solution methods. If the modes are well separated then non-linearities are only important when a single mode is responding around resonance and the eigenvector will often provide a good basis space for isolating the non-linearity to a single degree of freedom. Techniques are currently being developed to generalise this to the non-linear analysis with many modes but these are not fully developed and are unlikely to be found yet in any general purpose finite element system.

## 5.5 Static Condensation or Guyan Reduction

One common form of dynamic reduction available in most finite element systems is static condensation or Guyan reduction. In this form of reduction the stiffness properties of the structure are preserved exactly at the expense of its dynamic properties. It is widely used since it is easy and relatively cheap to carry out but it should be used with great caution since it is liable to introduce considerable, and not easily predictable, errors into the dynamic analysis.

For static condensation a set of master degrees of freedom are defined and these become the q displacements in the transformation equations. The remaining displacements are called the slave degrees of freedom and these are eventually eliminated from the solution process. There are many more slave degrees of freedom than masters. The transformation matrix, T, is constructed by applying a unit displacement to each degree of freedom in turn whilst setting all of the other master degrees of freedom to zero. The resulting slave displacements are used to define a column in T. This is repeated for each master in turn and the complete transformation matrix is constructed. It can be shown that this process preserves the static behaviour of the structure exactly. It is only approximate for the dynamic behaviour since the construction of the transformation matrix implicitly assumes that the inertia forces on the slave freedoms are zero. This has the effect of redistributing the mass of the slave freedoms onto the masters and there by altering the structural mass distribution. It is this assumption and its consequences that introduce all of the error into the Guyan reduction process. The error can be minimised by a selection of an optimum set of master degrees of freedom but it can never be eliminated.

## 5.6 Choice of Master Freedoms

Within a Guyan reduction the slave freedoms should be those that do not contribute much to the inertia forces in the dynamic response. The inertia forces are the product of mass and acceleration so that the slave freedoms should be those points of low mass or low acceleration. The statement can also be expressed as the master freedoms should be where the inertia forces are greatest. These tend to correspond to points of high mass and low stiffness. Some systems provide for an automatic selection of master freedoms by inspecting the ratio of corresponding diagonal terms of the stiffness and mass matrices, $K_{ii}/M_{ii}$. Master freedoms are then chosen as those equations where this ratio is smallest. Having a mass divisor will emphasise those points of high mass and multiplying by the stiffness emphasises the flexible parts of the structure where the acceleration is likely to be greatest. A choice of master freedoms based upon this or similar automatic considerations generally delivers a better set than those chosen by hand. The automatic choice however can fail if it concentrates all of the masters into one or two areas of the structure or if it concentrates them into a single direction. In these cases it is likely that the restrictions of such choices means that the resulting transformation matrix, $T$, will not adequately represent the eigenvectors and it will not allow the system to define the correct low frequency modes. Better results are obtained if the master freedoms are distributed over the structure. More sophisticated selection strategies are designed to overcome this problem.

## 5.7 Problems of Static Reduction

It is very difficult to quantify the errors associated with a static reduction. Generally the error in a given resonant frequency or mode shape will increase with eigenvalue number, that is the lowest eigenvalues are predicted better than the higher ones. However, this is not absolute and it sometimes happens that some higher modes are predicted more accurately than lower ones. Any predicted mode shape can only be a linear combination of the columns of the transformation matrix, $T$, and if this is deficient in a pattern of displacement required by a given mode shape then that mode will not be predicted accurately. The effect will always be to cause the eigenvalues of the condensed system to be greater than those of the original uncondensed system.

The fewer the number of master freedoms the greater the general error will be so that the user must choose a sufficient number of masters to minimise this, preferably the number of masters should be somewhere between two and ten times the number of modes that are required. Even with a factor of ten it is still very difficult to predict the consequence of the reduction in anything other than general terms. A choice of too many masters can lead cost problems. The original finite element equations are heavily banded and their sparse nature means that large sets of equations can be handled efficiently. The reduced transformed set will be fully populated so that, although fewer equations are involved they are much more densely packed and therefore more difficult to handle. If the original set of equations were of size n and average band width b then the number of master freedoms, m, should be satisfy $m^2 < bn$. If this is not the case then it would be cheaper computationally to work with the original set without any reduction. The cost of forming the reduced set must also be considered since this can be relatively expensive depending upon the form of implementation used. Normally advantage can be taken of the nature of the method to reduce the cost of forming the condensed stiffness matrix but the transformation must be carried out explicitly for the mass matrix.

## 5.8 Comments on Static Reduction

Instead of forming the transformation matrix by applying unit displacements at the master freedoms unit forces can be applied instead. It can be shown that this leads to identical final results as the standard Guyan reduction although the intermediate condensed matrices are different. Also the the method of subspace iteration for calculating the first few eigenvalues and eigenvectors of a system can be considered to be a repeated application of static condensation eliminating the assumption of zero mass on the slave freedoms. The first iteration of subspace iteration corresponds exactly to a static reduction. It is safer to use such an eigenvalue extraction technique (the Lanczos method being another one) on the full set of equations rather than using Guyan reduction methods, although theses sparse matrix methods can sometimes miss important modes in the analysis.

## 5.9 Dynamic Condensation

A small number of systems have a reduction process called dynamic condensation that attempts to combine modal reduction and static condensation. The disadvantage of modal reduction (apart from the cost of having to find the eigenvectors) is that it does not preserve the static behaviour of the structure in that the stiffness contribution from the modes that have been ignored is never reinstated. Static condensation suffers from the reverse problem of preserving the static stiffness at the expense of ignoring the dynamic effects. In dynamic condensation the transformation matrix, T, is largely based upon the eigenvectors associated with the lowest frequencies as with the modal reduction but these are augmented by static modes associated with master freedoms, as with static condensation. Generally the static modes have to be manipulated so that the stiffness associated with the lower modes that is accounted for by the presence of these modes is not included twice. This manipulation is easy to carry out using the Gramm-Scmidt orthonormalisation process. The resulting condensed equations of motion then have the better characteristics of both modal reduction and static condensation except that they are not diagonal as they are with modal reduction. The inclusion of the static modes plays a part directly parallel with the inclusion of residual flexibility terms when measured data results are synthesized into a numerical model. The main disadvantage of dynamic condensation over the other methods is that more equations are generated, although the parts of these associated with the modal reduction are heavily banded. However, it does give more accurate results. Dynamic condensation can be used in its own right but it is more often used with dynamic substructuring.

## 5.10 Advantages and Disadvantages of the Reduction Methods

The reason for using any form of reduction technique is to reduce the cost of the analysis. As a consequence of the cost reduction there is a loss of accuracy in the solution. The loss of accuracy always involve the omission of the higher resonant frequency response. The static reduction introduces other errors, notably, it tends to increase the values of the low frequency modes above their correct value and in some cases it can miss modes out entirely. The omission of the high frequency modes is not important for a displacement response but it becomes increasingly important for velocities and even more so for accelerations. The lack of high frequency mode shapes can also have the effect of underestimating the dynamic effects of stress concentrations.

## 5.11 Dynamic Substructuring

Another method of improving the computational efficiency of a dynamic analysis at the expense of accuracy is to use dynamic substructuring. This parallels exactly what is done for static substructuring in that the structure is divided into a series of smaller structures or substructures. The division into substructures is arbitrary but it is usually based upon a physical identification of components. For a static analysis it is always more efficient to substructure on surfaces that contain few nodes since this reduces the size of the component matrices. This is not always true for a dynamic analysis since the fewer the interface degrees of freedom the more approximation that is built into the dynamic representation. The consequence of this depends upon the exact form of dynamic substructuring that is being used and where dynamic modes are included in the substructure definition the greater the accuracy but the higher the cost.

At first sight it would seem that substructuring and the various forms of condensation methods are two different techniques but in practice they are very closely related. They both involve the construction, either directly or indirectly, of the transformation matrix **T**. With the various condensation methods there is no restriction on the form of this transformation matrix but for dynamic substructuring it has to satisfy some requirements. Most notably it is important that the various substructures can be assembled together. The simplest way of doing this is to follow the standard finite element assembly process which requires that the definition of the freedoms that are common between two components are identical. All of the substructures are referred to the same global axes and displacements on the connection faces are identical between the two components that are being connected. Note that it is often the users responsibility to ensure that the freedoms on the various components are defined relative to the same coordinate system. It is possible to assemble together components that are not in the same coordinate system but the results will be meaningless. In order to achieve the requirement of common freedoms the transformation matrix is usually defined in such a way as to preserve the original freedoms and it takes the form

$$\begin{bmatrix} r_1 \\ r_2 \end{bmatrix} = \begin{bmatrix} I & 0 \\ A & B \end{bmatrix} \begin{bmatrix} r_1 \\ q \end{bmatrix} \quad \text{so that} \quad T = \begin{bmatrix} I & 0 \\ A & B \end{bmatrix}$$

where $r_1$ are the freedoms that connect to other components, $r_2$ are freedoms that only connect to a single component and $q$ are freedoms internal to the reduced the component that are included to augment and improve the dynamic response. Note that with this form of definition of **T** the connection freedoms are preserved across the transformation and this makes the assembly of the various components to form the complete structure relatively easy. However, it does place restrictions upon the form of the transformation.

The simplest way of forming the subcomponent is to base the transformation upon the Guyan reduction. Here the master freedoms are not chosen arbitrarily but they are the connection freedoms. There are no augmenting freedoms, $q$, and the transformation matrix is identical to a Guyan reduction with the connection freedoms chosen as the master freedoms. This generally leads to a very poor dynamic approximation since the master freedoms are all clustered as the connection freedoms. This option of dynamic substructuring is often available in finite element systems but it should be avoided since it is so inaccurate.

## 5.12 Inclusion of Internal Modes in Dynamic Substructuring

The accuracy of the dynamic behaviour of a substructure can be improved considerably by including extra terms in the transformation matrix using the augmenting freedoms $q$. These are usually based upon some eigenvectors of the system so that the process becomes very similar to the dynamic condensation method described above. There are many ways of doing this and they all lead to different variations of the dynamic substructure method. It is very difficult to say which is the best method since they all give similar results and their relative accuracy depends upon the specific problem that is being analysed. The various forms of dynamic substructuring can be classified into one of two categories depending upon how the eigenvectors are formed. The most direct method is to calculate the eigenvectors of the substructure with the connection freedoms fixed. The alternative method is to calculate the eigenvectors of the substructure with the connection freedoms completely free.

## 5.13 Fixed Boundary Dynamic Substructures

If the eigenvectors of the substructure are found with the connection freedoms fixed so that they are all zero then the **B** matrix for the coordinate transformation just becomes the first few eigenvectors of the fixed boundary substructure. The number of augmenting freedoms is then equal to the number of these clamped modes that are included. The **A** term in the transformation matrix is found directly from the Guyan reduction process with the connection freedoms as masters. This means that the behaviour of the substructure is defined by its static behaviour for the connection freedoms and by its dynamic behaviour for the augmenting freedoms. There are still approximations involved in the representation of the dynamic behaviour of the substructure but these become progressively less significant as more eigenvectors are added to the augmenting set.

If a substructure has any global support points associated with it then these should be included in the substructure model both for the static reduction part and the eigenvector calculation. The fixed boundary dynamic substructure methods tend to be most accurate for those problems where all of the components have global support points associated with them. They are not so good for those problems where the substructures have no natural supports since the displacements of these substructures will be largely in terms of rigid body modes and fixed boundary substructures tend not to represent the rigid body mass of the components correctly.

## 5.14 Free Boundary Dynamic Substructure

The alternative to the fixed boundary form of substructure is the free boundary one. In this case the connection freedoms, $r_1$, are left free. The transformation matrix is defined in terms of the eigenvectors for the free boundary system. If the substructure has no natural supports then these eigenvectors will include the rigid body modes so that the rigid body mass of the structure is represented exactly. The free boundary substructure generally requires rather more calculations to form the transformation matrix. This form of dynamic substructure ensures that the mass description of the component is correct but the stiffness description is only approximate. The dynamic modes can then be augmented with static modes to recover the correct stiffness behaviour, at least for the connection freedoms. There seems to be indications that the free boundary dynamic substructure methods are more accurate than the fixed boundary ones but this is not clear cut and it does depend upon the precise form of the implementation of each method and the type of problem being solved. In practice most of the finite element systems that have dynamic substructuring available as an option tend to have a fixed boundary formulation since this is easier to implement.

## 5.15 Advantages and Disadvantages of Dynamic Substructures

Dynamic substructuring tends to have the same advantages and disadvantages that static substructuring has. A main advantage is that different analysts can be constructing models for the various components in parallel and thereby speeding up the analysis process. They only have to agree on the definition of the interface freedoms and the remainder of the finite element mesh within a component is independent of the other components. There are great advantages when one component is repeated many times within a model since it need only be generated once. The discussion given here assumes that the components are joined together in a simple node to node finite element assembly form. This need not be the case and it is possible to use sophisticated forms of generalised constraints to join together components with dissimilar meshes. The use of substructuring makes this an easier task than if it were attempted without substructuring.

One of the main disadvantages of dynamic substructuring is also the same as for static substructures and that is the problems associated with handling and controlling the data for all of the substructures. It is necessary to form the substructures independently, to assemble them into the global model, solve the global model and then to feed the results of this back to the individual components to recover the response and stresses within the components. This requires considerable amounts of data handling and the feasibility of using dynamic substructuring then depends upon the help that the system provides for controlling the data. Typically a set of disc files can be generated for each component and they must all be retained and accessed in the correct sequence for the whole analysis to work. If dynamic substructuring is to be used in anything other than one off situations then this must be automated.

## 5.16 Modal Synthesis

Modal synthesis is the same as modal reduction discussed earlier. In order to use this the analyst must choose the number of modes that are to be calculated and employed in any response calculations. To do this some guidance is required in what is the correct number of modes to choose. If too few are taken then there will be errors in the resulting response calculations. If too many are chosen then the cost of calculating all of the eigenvalues and eigenvectors will be excessive.

# CHAPTER 6 - DYNAMIC TESTING

## 6.1 Introduction

There are two main reasons why an analyst is interested in experimental dynamic testing. One is to verify the computational results and give confidence in the model and the second is to provide information to help with the dynamic modelling. This information can be either just an indication of which parts of the structure are dynamically active and what the typical frequencies are, or it can provide measured data that is used within the computational model for components that are difficult to model analytically. One important point to bear in mind when considering experimental results is that any experimental set up contains simplifications and approximations to the in-service conditions in the same way that a finite element model does. When comparing computed and measured results it is rare for them to agree in detail. In many cases this is because the assumptions within the computational model and the requirements of the experimental set up are not the same and this leads to the differences. It is possible for both the experimental model and the computational model to not agree with each other but for them both to be correct within their own right. Where both a computational and a testing program are being conducted it is essential that the two teams work together and communicate freely. A great deal of time and effort can be wasted by a lack of communication if this results in significant differences between the computational and experimental models.

Dynamic testing requires as much expertise as finite element modelling in order to obtain reliable results. If two experienced experimental groups test the same structure then they will not obtain identical results, in the same way that if two experienced finite element groups model the same structure they will not obtain identical results either. The same form of results interpretation is required when comparing experimental and analytic results as when interpreting different finite element results.

## 5.2 Types of Experimental Tests

Some quantities are easier to measure dynamically than others. Probably the simplest quantities to measure are the resonant frequencies of the structure, together with the associated mode shapes. The steady state response of the structure at one point to a sinusoidal force applied at another can also be measured. The transient time variation of the response can be measured but this becomes increasingly difficult as the frequency content of the response rises. These tests tend to require different experimental techniques. The form of support conditions can also be important in dynamic testing. Probably the least ambiguous is the free-free structure, that is, one where ideally the structure is not supported at all. It is very difficult to achieve a clamped support dynamically in an experimental set up and the stiffer the support requirement then the more difficult it is to achieve. The response is usually measured with accelerometers so that the structural accelerations are the basic measured quantities. These can be integrated to give the velocities and displacements but this is not very accurate for low frequency response, typically below about 1Hz, where noise and drift in the instrumentation can affect the integrated results. In such cases, for low frequency response, it is better to use displacement transducers. These are not accurate at higher frequencies since the displacement response is too low in this regime. The accelerometers measure the direct translational behaviour. Experimentally it is very difficult to measure the rotational response. Many attempts have been made to do this but so far none have been completely successful and the errors associated with rotational response measurements are always much higher than those associated with the translational response.

### 5.2.1 Measuring Resonant Frequencies and Mode Shapes

Modal testing forms a very large part of dynamic testing. The response of a linear structure is completely characterised by its resonant frequencies and associated mode shapes and if these are measured accurately then the dynamic response of the structure can be computed. There are many variations within the precise experimental details as to how they are measured but they all rely upon the same basic dynamic theory. If a single degree of freedom system with a small amount of viscous damping or with hysteretic material damping is excited by an harmonic forcing function then its steady state response can be

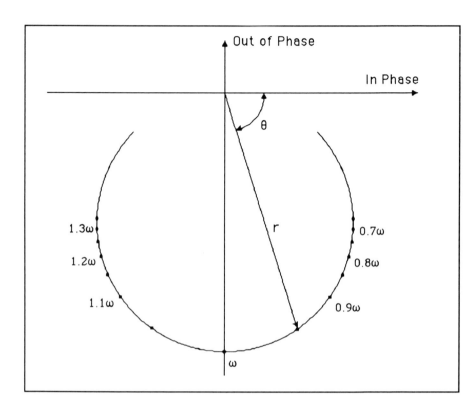

<u>Fig 6.1 - Polar Plot of the Harmonic Response</u>

measured. This response will not have the same phase as the forcing function because of the damping so that two quantities have to be measured, either the in phase and out of phase amplitudes of the response or the total amplitude of the response and its phase relative to the forcing function. If a polar plot of the amplitude and phase is made then a response similar to that shown in figure 6.1 is obtained. This is a circle for lightly damped linear systems.

For the idealised one degree of freedom system having the Nyquist plot shown in figure 6.1 the resonant frequency, $\omega$, occurs at a phase angle of ninety degrees, where the in phase component of the response is zero. In practice the effect of other modes is to shift the centre of the circle and to rotate the axes by some amount so that this is not a good way of defining the resonance. A much more accurate method relies upon the fact that it can be shown that the spacing between equal frequency squared increment points (and for typical very light damping this approximates closely to equal frequency increments) around the circle is greatest at resonance. This gives a very sensitive and accurate method for locating the resonant frequency. The rate of change of the frequency around the response circle allows the damping of the system to be measured accurately.

Some systems excite the structure with a discrete sine wave, others with random white noise, yet others with a swept sine wave and some have an impulsive hammer strike. In all cases the response can be processed to give the response circle similar to the one shown. If there are two or more close resonant frequencies then the response circles can merge together but it is usually still possible to identify the separate resonant frequencies. All points on the structure should exhibit a similar polar response plot and the ratios of the circle diameters for different points allow the mode shape to be measured.

This response curve assumes low damping and that the damping in the modes do not couple, that is, proportional, damping is assumed. If the damping is not proportional then each point on the structure reaches its maximum displacement at a different phase angle and the modes are complex so that the response at any point has an amplitude and a phase angle. If the damping is relatively large then, for viscous damping, the response becomes less and less circular and is increasingly difficult to interpret. However, it should be noted that the Nyquist plot also becomes less circular as the non-linearity in the system increases.

Where the modes are distinct and lightly damped this measuring and presentation technique gives an extremely accurate and sensitive method for measuring resonant frequencies and mode shapes.

## 5.2.2 The Frequency Response

A similar experimental procedure to that used for measuring the resonant frequency can also be used to measure the frequency response of the structure. This is found by exciting the structure at a single point over a range of frequencies and measuring the response. Two plots are produced for each point. The first is the steady state amplitude against frequency and the second the phase angle against frequency. A plot of the steady state acceleration per unit force is called the inertance, a similar plot of velocity against frequency is the mobility and the displacement plot is called the receptance. Obviously all three are related via the frequency or the frequency squared. The experiment is repeated for the exciting force at each location in turn so that eventually an (nxn) set of plots are produced, where there are n location points. Taking the receptance all (nxn) points at a single frequency, $\omega$, will give after inversion, the dynamic stiffness at that frequency. This can be used together with the analytical model to combine the experimental and the analytical models. One practical difficulty here is the fact that it is difficult to measure the rotational response so that the full dynamic stiffness matrix cannot be measured. This limits the practical usefulness of the measured dynamic stiffness matrix.

### 6.2.3 The Transient Response

One of the problems with the experimental determination of the transient response is associated with the definition of the force input. Ideally either a true impulse or a sharp step change is required but these are impossible to achieve exactly. Deviations from this ideal tends to limit the accuracy of the high frequency components of the response. One quantity that can be measured from the transient response is the wave speed within the structure and this partly characterises the transient response. There are various sets of shock tests with specific shock spectra defined but these are not so useful from the analyst's point of view. They form environmental tests and are normally used as go/no-go type tests in that the equipment is not instrumented but it is shown to operate normally after the test. As such this provides no useful information to the analyst. For a linear system the transient impulse response can be obtained from a Fourier transformation of the dynamic stiffness so that the transient response can be found from the frequency response. It is interesting to note that the impulse response of the structure is best found by exciting the structure with random white noise. If the response at any point is then cross correlated with the force input the resulting cross correlation is the impulse response at the measurement point to an impulse applied at the excitation point.

## 6.3 Use of Tests to Guide Finite Element Analysis

With real structures it is often very difficult to decide how best to model the structure for a dynamic analysis. If a structure is available for testing purposes then relatively simple low level hammer tests can be used to identify the important resonant frequencies and which parts of the structure are responding. The structure does not need to be identical to the one under analysis provided that it is similar. Such information can be invaluable in guiding the analyst as to the important characteristics that should be modelled. Typical resonant frequencies and relative amplitudes of different points on the structure can be measured. Since the structure in this case is assumed to be in situ rather than being tested under laboratory conditions the exact nature of such aspects as boundary conditions will not be well defined so the analyst should not expect to reproduce the results of these tests exactly from any analysis. The tests can help the analyst to decide which components can be treated as rigid blocks on flexible supports and which have to be modelled in more dynamic detail. They can also be used to indicate which components interact dynamically.

A low level test can also be used to determine the level of damping within the structure. For most structures the damping mechanisms are not well defined and damping is hard to model. If the typical damping values are measured by simple test then the resulting modal damping values can be used in the analysis to give representative damping. In most cases a knowledge of the order of magnitude of the damping is sufficient and simple hammer tests are sufficiently accurate to give working values for the modal damping.

## 6.4 Comparison of Analysis Results and Test Results

One purpose of conducting dynamic tests, especially modal testing, is to confirm the dynamic analysis model by comparing the computed resonant frequencies and mode shapes with the measured ones. In order for such a comparison to be valid care must be taken to ensure that the analysis model and the test model are comparable. If the structure is supported it is common for the analyst to assume that the support conditions are rigid. In a practical experimental set up it is very difficult to achieve a rigid support condition. To illustrate this a cantilever beam was analysed using a rigid support and one where it is built into a heavy plate as it might be in an experimental set up. This plate is clamped rigidly

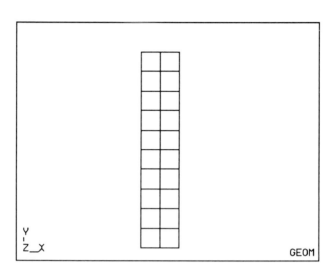

Fig 6.2 - Fixed End Cantilever

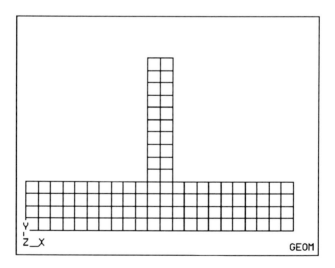

Fig 6.3 - Flexible End  Cantilever

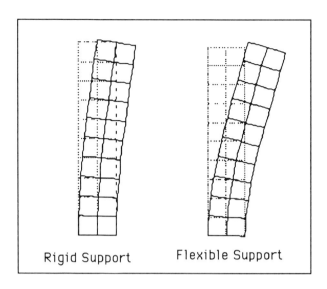

Fig 6.4 - First Mode Shape for Rigid and Flexible Support

| | Resonant Frequencies | | |
|---|---|---|---|
| Mode | Rigid Support (Hz) | Flexible Support (Hz) | Flexible/Rigid |
| 1 | 32.2 | 30.8 | 0.957 |
| 2 | 174.2 | 166.6 | 0.956 |
| 3 | 256.3 | 238.7 | 0.931 |
| 4 | 416.9 | 389.2 | 0.934 |
| 5 | 696.2 | 466.3 | 0.670 |
| 6 | 766.7 | 612.1 | 0.798 |

Table 6.1 - Cantilever Frequencies with Rigid and Flexible End

along its base and on the vertical edges. The two models are shown in figures 6.2 and 6.3. The comparative frequencies are given in table 6.1. Note that there are significant differences in the two set of frequencies even though the finite element model with the 'flexible' support will still be stiffer than could be achieved by most experimental set ups. There is very little difference in the mode shapes as will be seen in figure 6.4 where they are both displayed. (These plots are slightly misleading in that the deflected shapes were scaled by different amounts when producing the plot). In practice the actual shapes are very nearly identical and it would not be possible to detect that the support was flexible from the measured results.

## 6.5  Modal  Testing

The testing methods described in sections 6.2.1 and 6.2.2 are generally referred to as modal testing. If the structural response is linear then a careful application of any of these techniques will lead to reliable results for resonant frequencies, mode shapes and related quantities. If there is any significant non-linearities in the system then a great deal of care must be taken in interpreting the results, especially for any method that processes the results using a Fourier transform. This assumes that superposition is valid which is not the case for non-linear systems. Unfortunately the signal processing attempts to produce the results in a linear form and this can disguise the real results. As with all forms of dynamic testing care must be taken with the support conditions and the method that is used to excite the structure since these can affect the results. Surveys have been conducted by getting various research groups to measure the dynamic response of the same structure and it has been found that there can be significant scatter on the results from various groups. This tends to have very little correlation with the test method used and is more related to how the structure was supported and excited. What is of interest to the finite element analyst is that those models that presented difficulties of measurement also present difficulties of analysis. Typically, a structure with flexible joints is difficult to analyse accurately and it is equally difficult to measure its dynamics characteristics accurately.

The modal testing results can be presented in various ways, one form being the mobility, $Y(\omega)$, which is defined as

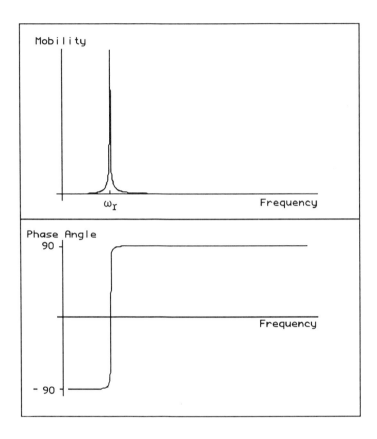

Fig 6.5 Variation of Mobility and Associated Phase Angle with Frequency

$$Y(\omega) = \frac{\dot{g}e^{i\omega t}}{Ge^{i\omega t}} = \frac{\dot{g}}{G} = \frac{\text{velocity}}{\text{force}}$$

where $\dot{g}$ is the velocity amplitude at the frequency $\omega$ and G is the amplitude of the exciting force. The ratio of the displacement amplitude, g, to the force is called the receptance and the ratio of the acceleration, $\ddot{g}$, to the force is the inertance or accelerance. For a linear system if any one of these three are known at a given frequency then the other two can be found. For any real system or a numerical model with damping all three of these quantities will be complex. The real part is the in phase component of the response and the imaginary

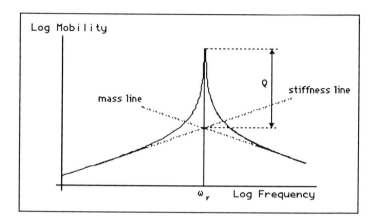

Fig 6.6 - Log Mobility Modulus Plot

part is the out of phase component. This can also be expressed as the total amplitude, that is, the square root of the sum of the squares of the real and imaginary parts and the phase angle. The tangent of the phase angle is the ratio of the real to the imaginary parts. In practice the inertance is the most commonly measured quantity since accelerometers are used as the measuring transducers.

For a one degree of freedom system a typical mobility plot in terms of amplitude and phase angle is shown in figure 6.5. The large amplitude of the response means that it is often more common to plot this using logarithmic axes and the same mobility plot is given in figure 6.6 in this form. At low frequency the log plot shows that the response is defined by the structural stiffness and at high frequencies by the structural mass. At resonance damping becomes important. The Q-factor is the amplification obtained at resonance and this is inversely proportional to the damping in the system.

## 6.6  Comparison  with  Theory

Model verification is probably the most frequent requirement of experimental testing so far as an analyst is concerned, although there are times when tests have to be conducted to provided numerical data (typically damping data) to be used in the analysis. Testing is often carried out on models or just parts of the structure to validate the analysis method rather than confirm the final results. If such verification confirms the accuracy of the model then a greater degree of confidence in the finite element model is generated. However, complete agreement is rarely, if ever, obtained so that a second objective of the test/theory comparison becomes one of identifying the reasons for such differences and deciding if they require any alterations be made to the model. If a part of the test is used to obtain damping values then these should usually only be treated as order of magnitude values since, for most structural systems, the damping is low and is affected by both the test and in service operating conditions.

## 6.7 Identifying Natural Frequencies and Mode Shapes

One of the easier set of quantities to compute within a dynamic analysis are the natural frequencies and the mode shapes. These can also be found experimentally using the polar (Nyquist) plots discussed in section 6.3. It is then reasonable to compare the table of calculated resonant frequencies with the corresponding table of measured frequencies and assess the differences. Unfortunately, life is rarely as simple as this and frequently the comparison is not straightforward. There are many reasons why there is not an immediate one to one comparison between theory and experiment, the main ones being:

1. The real structure is almost invariably more complicated than the finite element model. Items that have been modelled as rigid for the finite element analysis can be flexible, typically a structure may have a small electric motor bolted on to it. This is mainly a rigid lump and can be idealised as such but the shaft can move on the bearings and this can cause modifications to the measured response compared to the finite element model response.

2. For a natural frequency calculation the structural response is assumed to be linear. The measured response need not follow this assumption.

3. For a real structure the response can be quite complicated with modes typically being classified as a set bending about the x-axis, another set bending about the

y-axis and a third being torsion of the structure. Very often the finite element idealisation is not to the same order of accuracy for all of these different motions so that it is quite possible for the finite element model to be giving a significantly higher error in its estimate of say the torsion mode frequencies than those for the bending modes. In this case the comparison between theory and experiment will be good for bending and poor for torsion. The values of the various resonant frequencies in the different sets of modes tend to interleave so that it is quite possible to have a very good agreement for say, the first, third and sixth modes but poor agreement with the second, fourth and fifth.

4.  Some parts of the structure can resonate in local modes, confined to one small area. Such modes can be missed or be very inaccurate within the finite element model. This problem is essentially the same as the the first given in this list and, if the local mode is to be included in the finite element model, then a modification to the mesh is required.

5.  The support conditions and excitation conditions can be different between the real structure and the finite element model. A common difference here is to assume that the supports are rigid in the model. In the real structure this is rarely the case. Again, such assumptions often affect some modes more than others and causes the accuracy of the comparison between theory and experiment to be inconsistent.

There are many other reasons as to why there is not an exact agreement between analysis and test results. This makes it important to carry out such comparisons carefully and to use judgment as to the significance of the the differences. If they are due to secondary effects they can be ignored but if they are due to errors in the finite element model then it is possible that the model should be modified to account such errors. The main difficulty here is that, after identifying differences between test and theory, it is still very difficult to decide what is causing the difference and hence what to modify.

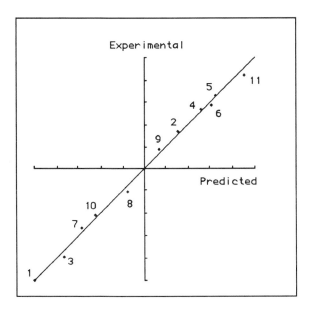

Fig 6.7 - Comparison of Predicted and Measured Mode Shape

## 6.8 The Modal Assurance Criterion

Before any comparison is made between resonant frequencies the analyst must be sure that like with like is being compared. Two frequencies might compare well but if one is for a bending mode and the other for a torsion mode then the comparison is meaningless. This means that both frequencies and modes should be compared simultaneously. For anything other than simple structures it is difficult to compare the actual mode shapes directly as distorted plots. Such a comparison can give a general impression from a qualitative point of view in that it can be seen if the modes are symmetric or antisymmetric or if they are bending or torsion but it does not provide any quantitative data on how well they compare. This requires that the modes are compared numerically in some manner. Say there are two estimates for the same mode, one predicted and one measured (note that they could both be predicted or both measured if required) and they have been normalised in the same manner. Preferably they have been mass normalised so that $\phi^t M \phi = 1$ in both cases. If not then the maximum displacement is unity in both cases. A plot is then made of the measured mode against the predicted mode, as shown in figure 6.7. Each point corresponds to the response of a given point in the predicted and the calculated modes. If the modes correlate exactly then these points will form a straight line at 45 degrees to the axis. The deviation of the points from this line then gives a measure of the lack of correlation. If the modes are mass normalised and there is some error in the normalising factor then the points will form a straight line at some angle other than 45 degrees. If some points lie on a straight line but others do not then it can be useful to superimpose plots from various modes onto a single graph. Any systematic error in either the test results or the finite element results will then show up for some points having an error in all modes.

The least squares deviation of the points from the best straight line gives the Modal Assurance Criterion (MAC). If the normalised experimental mode shape for the j'th mode is $\phi_{xj}$ and the normalised j'th mode as predicted by the finite element results is $\phi_{pj}$ then the modal assurance criterion is

$$\text{MAC(p,x,j)} = \frac{(\phi_{xj} \, \bar{\phi}_{pj}^{t})^2}{(\phi_{xj} \, \bar{\phi}_{xj}^{t} \, \phi_{pj} \, \bar{\phi}_{pj}^{t})}$$

where the bar denotes complex conjugate if the measured mode is a damped mode with the displacements having different phase angles. If the modes are completely correlated then the MAC is unity. If it tends to zero then the modes are not correlated.

## 6.9  Use of the Modal Assurance Criterion

The main use of the MAC is to identify which frequencies should be compared between theory and experiment. Say over a frequency range 0 to $\omega_c$ there are n measured frequencies and modes and m calculated ones. The MAC can be applied between all measured and all computed modes, giving an (nxm) MAC matrix. If n>m then the matrix can be inspected by looking down the m columns and if n<m then it is inspected by looking across the n rows. Frequencies can then be compared between theory and experiment for those rows and columns that have a MAC value close to unity. A good MAC value is in the range 0.9 to 1 but values less than this can be expected in reality. If in a given row or

column that is being inspected there are two values close to unity, then the larger one should be taken with the other mode being interpreted as a repeat of the actual mode shape, probably caused by one of the reasons listed in section 6.7. This can also be caused by not having enough measurement points to uniquely identify a mode, as discussed in section 6.10. If, in a given row or column, there is no MAC value close to unity then the mode is unique to either the theory or the experiment. In this case further investigation should be made. If the mode only appears in the experimental set then check the mode shape. In some circumstances, especially using modern automated transfer function analysers, a numerical curve fitting process can generate spurious modes. Generally these have a very poorly defined polar response plot and can be discarded. In other cases they can be a well defined mode which has been missed by the finite element model. This might be because it is a local mode, in which case the finite element model is probably still quite acceptable if all of the other modes correlate, or it could be a full structural mode, in which case the finite element model probably needs to be modified. Often this arises because the finite element model assumes an ideal situation. Typically, if a large point mass is place exactly on the centre line of a cantilever beam then it will not excite torsional oscillations. However, if the mass is slightly offset from the centre line then a low frequency torsional mode can result. Such an imperfect structure is much more likely to occur in practice than the perfect one and, being sensitive to imperfections in the location of the mass centre of gravity, gives different practical results. Where a structure is sensitive to imperfections from the ideal then the consequences of such imperfections should be investigated. Other such idealisations often include assumptions of perfect symmetry or antisymmetry. If only the symmetric modes of a finite element model are computed then there will be discrepancies between theory and test. No matter how much care is taken in the experiment both symmetric and antisymmetric modes will be identified and there will be some lack of correlation. This can be corrected by computing all of the theoretical modes over a given frequency range.

It is also quite possible to have more computed than measured modes within a frequency range. In the experiment accelerometers are often placed to measure the response normal to the surface of the structure. A triaxial set of three accelerometers per point gives a better measurement but, due to the cost and the limited number of signal conditioning channels, such a set up might not be used. If the measurements are only taken normal to the surface of the structure then it is possible to miss in-plane extensional type modes experimentally. It is also possible to apply an excitation to a point that has a null response for a given mode and that mode will not be excited. In all such cases, because of the non-ideal nature of the real structure, there should be some measured response but in practice it might be very difficult to clearly identify this.

When comparing between theory and experiment it is as well to have experimental results at two or more levels of excitation. This will provide evidence as to the degree of non-linearity in the response of the real structure. Any theoretical normal mode prediction assumes a completely linear response. If the real response is only mildly non-linear then a linear assumption should be quite good. However, if the actual response is significantly non-linear or is sensitive to small degrees of non-linear behaviour then the theoretical values might not be valid. Wherever possible it is also a good idea to have experimental results where the method of excitation and possibly the method of support has been changed to give some measure of the sensitivity of the experimental results to the experimental set up.

## 6.10  Choosing Measurement Locations

The modal assurance criterion can be very useful in deciding the best locations to place the limited number of measurement transducers that are usually available. The analysis model allows the mode shapes to be computed at many more locations than can be measured. The experimentalist can take advantage of this by using the computed mode shapes at the points where it is proposed to place accelerometers and the carrying out a modal assurance criterion test on these condensed vectors. If the locations chosen provide a unique identification of the modes then this will show in the results of the MAC. However, if the choice of measurement points is deficient then the MAC will not give a unique identification of the modes. The positions of the measurement points can then be varied until a suitable set is found. This, together with the fact that the computed results give the frequency range of importance, indicates another reason why the testing and the analysis should proceed together rather than being conducted independently in isolation from each other.

## 6.11 Assessment of Modelling Errors

The MAC is used to identify which modes should be compared between two sets of results. Use of some of the preceding arguments can resolve some of the reasons for discrepancies between theory and experiment but it can still leave some modes which are important but where the agreement between theory and experiment needs to be improved. An initial action to take here is to inspect the modes with significant differences to see if they have the same characteristics in common, say, they are all bending about the x axis. This would indicate that the finite element model is deficient in some respect for this behaviour. The mesh might not be fine enough, the element used might not allow the correct behaviour in this direction or the supports might be too rigid. If this can be identified then the model can be modified accordingly. Unfortunately, such a simple clear cut solution as this is rarely the case and more sophisticated methods of investigation are required. If all of the resonance frequencies are are only in moderate agreement with none being especially good or especially poor then this indicates that a general mesh improvement is required. If the agreement gets worse as the mode number increases then more elements are required. If the error is about the same for all modes then more attention to the detailed modelling such as mass distribution, offset modelling and connection details is probably necessary. A much better agreement between some modes than others probably indicates that only parts of the model need to be changed.

The alternatives are to investigate possible modelling errors in the stiffness distribution, the mass distribution, the support conditions and the experimental test environment. There is no point in trying to investigate individual terms in the mass or stiffness matrices since they are obtained from highly idealised finite element assumptions and have little or no physical significance as individual numbers. What is more relevant is to condense the finite element stiffness and mass matrices to the measured degrees of freedom and to use the measured frequencies and mode shapes to obtain experimental estimates of the stiffness and mass matrices such that theoretically and experimentally these are available at the same points and in the same directions. If the condensed theoretical stiffness matrix is $K_p$ and the condensed mass matrix is $M_p$ and the corresponding measured matrices are $K_x$ and $M_x$ then the difference matrices (sometimes called error matrices) are:

$$K_\Delta = K_p - K_x$$

$$M_\Delta = M_p - M_x$$

The terms in these difference matrices can then be investigated and if the differences for some degrees of freedom are much larger than for others then it indicates that the differences between the finite element model and the real structure is in the vicinity of these points. If the points are close to support points (which is not usually the case because experimental measurement points tend to be away from the supports) or near the excitation positions then it is quite possible that the differences are more associated with the experimental set up, or at least the differences that arise from the test requirements, rather than being inherent within the model. Alternatively, if the points of difference are within the body of the structure then this indicates deficiencies in the finite element model which should be modified accordingly. In practice these techniques leave a lot to be desired for real structures and the differences tend to be spread evenly throughout $K_\Delta$ and $M_\Delta$ rather than at specific points. This is partly due to the the fact that both the finite element condensation process or an experimental model expansion tend to smear  the errors over the complete matrix. The condensation process itself is not exact and tends to introduce further errors that are not present in the complete model.

There is little point in using the difference matrices, $K_\Delta$ and $M_\Delta$ to 'correct' the analytical matrices $K_p$ and $M_p$. The analytical matrices have been obtained by condensing the basic finite element matrices to the measurement points. There is no reliable way of expanding this condensed information back to the full equation set. It makes little difference whether the expansion is in terms of expanding the measured mode shapes to the full size by some interpolation process or the difference matrices are expanded from the condensed equations the resulting equations are not very realistic.

In the long term a better approach consists of identifying what the differences are sensitive to by using first order sensitivity equations. The same approach can be used if the analyst suspects some assumptions made during the process of idealising to the finite element model, such as member stiffnesses of mass lumping approximations, by seeing how sensitive the results are to changing these assumptions. The first order sensitivity matrix gives the change in the i'th eigenvalue due to some small change $\Delta K$ in the stiffness matrix and some small change $\Delta M$ in the mass matrix as

$$\lambda_{i\Delta} = \frac{\phi^t_i ( \Delta K - \lambda_i \Delta M ) \phi_i}{\phi^t_i M \phi_i}$$

where $\lambda_i$ and $\phi_i$ are the i'th eigenvalue and corresponding eigenvector for the original system. Unfortunately there are many parameters defining a finite element model and it is impossible to vary them all to investigate all aspects of the sensitivity for even a few resonant frequencies. Where possible the difference matrices or the uncertainties that the analyst has about the model should be used is to restrict the number of parameters that have to be investigated when looking at the sensitivities. In these regions a single parameter, say the thickness of a plate or the stiffness of a joint, can be modified and the change in all of the eigenvalues that arises can be found. If there is little change then this parameter can be discarded. However, if the frequencies that are in disagreement between theory and test are altered by the change but the frequencies that agree are not then it is very probable that the source of the difference has been identified. Using this technique and with a degree of luck and good judgement the sensitive parameters can be found and the effect of combining them can be investigated to produce an improved model. The calculation of the sensitivity is relatively cheap because it only involves matrix multiplications. It is even cheaper if mass normalisation is used so that $\phi^t_i M \phi_i = 1$. When suitable values of some parameters have been found then the eigenvalue problem using the modified equations should be solved since the sensitivity term is only correct to first order. This process can be made more automatic if a structural optimisation procedure is available since it is essentially the same as optimising the structure with the objective function being to make the differences between the computed and the measured eigenvalues as small as possible.

## 6.12 In-Service Vibration Measurements

In some circumstances it is not possible to carry out a modal test, typically because the plant is too large or is inaccessible. In this case monitoring equipment such as accelerometers can be placed onto the equipment while it is working. This does not represent a true dynamic test because the loading is not controlled or even known in many cases. The response under operating conditions can be measured at various points and the measured time histories subject to a frequency or spectral density analysis. This will produce peaks in the response but these peaks can be due either to resonances or due to the loading itself being concentrated in some frequency bands. Where possible results should be obtained under different operating conditions and a strong frequency response that occurs in all of the results is more likely to be a resonance. Measuring the response simultaneously at various points on the plant allows an estimate of the mode shapes to be found. These should be inspected to see if they make sense. Typically, if the plant is a building then bending and torsion modes should be identified in the first few mode shapes. It is very much more difficult to interpret the results of any in-service vibration measurements than it is from a modal test because only a part of the data is known. It is to be expected that there is a significantly worse agreement for comparisons between in-service measurements and theory than for modal testing and theory. However, it is still better to try and correlate such in service measurements with theory rather than having no practical results at all since, provided care is taken in their interpretation, they can still help to increase confidence in the finite element model.


## 6.13  Seeking  Help


One draw back with correlating test and theory that occurs in most large organisations is that the two sets of results are found by different groups. This can then lead naturally to some degree of antagonism or defensiveness between the groups when discrepancies are identified with little intercommunication occurring. This should be avoided at all costs. Discrepancies can arise from so many sources that the two groups should have a clear understanding of what each other is doing to avoided clouding the issue by misunderstandings so that like is not being compared with like. A frequent problem here is the analyst assuming a totally rigid support but the test having a stiff but not rigid support. The sets of results should be discussed by the two groups where they are seeking to help each other to find the reasons for any differences rather than to defend their results. Both groups should be prepared to modify their approach to investigate possible reasons for differences. This produces very positive benefits in the future in that both sets of people have a better understanding of a wider aspect of dynamic analysis. Since the number of possibilities for difference between test and theory is legion it can be very useful to seek the help of people with experience of other dynamic problems. Very often explaining what was done to a third party helps to point towards reasons for any discrepancies even if the third party has no direct experience of the problem.

An understanding of both the theoretical results and the analysis process together with a similar understanding of the test results and the experimental process will always give a better insight into dynamic problems. The dynamic problem has so many possibilities for misunderstanding and wrong interpretation that collaboration should be sought at all stages to broaden everybody's understanding of the process. Usually neither the experimental nor the computational results are 'exact' in representing real life but an understanding as to why they differ helps to extrapolate to the real life situation.

# CHAPTER 7 - DAMPING

## 7.1 Introduction

When a real structure vibrates the total energy in the system (the sum of the kinetic and potential energies) will always be decreasing if no external force is applied. This loss of energy by the system is given the general term damping. There are many different mechanisms within a vibrating structure that give rise to energy dissipation but three general possibilities can be defined

1.  Some specific form of energy dissipation has been designed into the structure. This usually means that the amount of energy dissipated per cycle of vibration is relatively high. It also means that the damping mechanism is well defined and can probably be included within the finite element model.

2.  There is no specific energy dissipation mechanism built into the structure but the natural forms of energy dissipation can be identified and modelled. Again, the damping can usually be included directly into the finite element model in this case.

3.  There is no specific energy dissipation mechanism built into the structure and the natural damping mechanisms are not easily identified or quantified. Usually in this case there is more than one damping mechanism present and they all dissipate relatively little energy per cycle. This is the most common situation that is encountered within a structural dynamic system.

The problem of assessing damping is further complicated by the fact that it can be difficult to differentiate experimentally between small damping values and low levels of non-linearities within the response. This makes it difficult to measure the low levels of damping often encountered and can help to explain the large variations in quoted damping values given by different sources.

## 7.2 Energy Dissipation

All analytical models for damping utilise the fact that a force which is a function of the velocity of the structural response will dissipate energy. The equation of motion with damping can be written as

$$m\ddot{r} + F(\dot{r}) + kr = R$$

where $F(\dot{r})$ is some function of the structural velocity $\dot{r}$. The form of the function used depends upon how well the analyst can define the damping process itself. If this can be done in detail then a detailed damping model can be constructed. There are varying degrees of approximation that are used in practice depending upon how well the damping is defined, how high the damping is (how much energy it dissipates each cycle) and what facilities are available within the analysis program that are available for modelling damping.

## 7.3 Viscous Damping

The simplest damping representation is one where the damping is proportional to velocity.

$$m\ddot{r} + c\dot{r} + kr = R$$

where c is called the viscous damping coefficient. For linear damping models it is taken as being constant. Although viscous damping is the simplest model that will dissipate energy it does represent real forms of damping. Energy carried away by acoustic radiation from the structure and by fluid flowing over a structure both give rise to viscous damping.

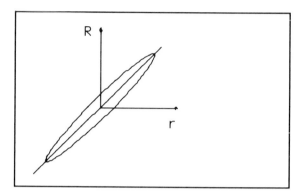

Fig 7.1 - Energy Dissipation for Viscous Damping

*7.3.1 Steady state response with viscous damping*

If the structure is excited by an harmonic forcing function at a frequency, $\omega$, then the equation of motion with viscous damping is

$$m\ddot{r} + c\dot{r} + kr = Ge^{i\omega t}$$

and the steady state response after all of the transients have died away is

$$r = ge^{i\omega t}$$

where

$$g = \frac{G}{(k - \omega^2 m + i\omega c)}$$

The real part of g is the component of the response that has the same phase as the exciting force and the imaginary component of the response is ninety degrees out of phase with the exciting force,

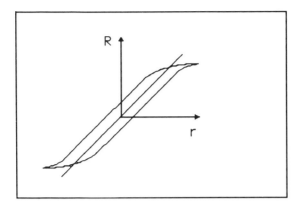

Figure 7.2 - Hysteretic Response Loop

*7.3.2 Energy dissipated per cycle by viscous damping*

For a steady state response the energy dissipated per cycle is $E = \pi \omega c r^2$ The energy dissipated is directly proportional to the excitation frequency and the damping coefficient and is proportional to the square of the response amplitude. A plot of the variation of displacement against applied force has an elliptical shape, as shown in figure 7.1. The area enclosed by the ellipse is equal to the energy dissipated per cycle.

## 7.4    Material (Hysteretic) Damping

When a material is loaded cyclically then it is found that the resulting stress strain curve describes an hysteresis loop, as shown in figure 7.2. The energy dissipated per cycle is proportional to the area enclosed by the curve. The sharp corners on the curve means that the response is non-linear and the material damping is linearised by replacing the hysteretic loop by an ellipse with the same enclosed area. However, it is found experimentally that the energy dissipated per cycle by internal energy dissipation is independent of the frequency of excitation. This is unlike viscous damping where the energy dissipated is proportional to frequency. To give the correct model material damping is idealised as a viscous damping coefficient divided by the frequency of excitation

$$c = \frac{h}{\omega}$$

and the equation of motion is

$$m\ddot{r} + \left\{\frac{h}{\omega}\right\}\dot{r} + kr = Ge^{i\omega t}$$

Note that this form of material damping (or hysteretic damping as it is sometimes called) is only valid if the frequency $\omega$ is defined. The material damping model is only valid for an harmonic excitation and has no meaning for other types of excitation. Since the model is only valid for harmonic motion then an alternative form of the material damping model is the complex stiffness form where the equation of motion is

$$m\ddot{r} + (k + ih)r = Ge^{i\omega t}$$

and the constant h is exactly the same as in the previous equation. Again this model is only valid for harmonic excitation. For other forms of excitation the conventional form of viscous damping must be used.

### 7.4.1 Steady state response with material damping

The steady state response of a system with material damping is

$$r = ge^{i\omega t}$$

where

$$g = \frac{G}{(k - \omega^2 m + ih)}$$

For light damping at one frequency typical of structural vibrations this response is difficult to distinguish from the response for viscous damping. In this case the energy dissipated per cycle is $E = \pi \eta r^2$ and is independent of frequency which is consistent with the initial assumption used to define the material damping.

## 7.5  Coulomb Damping

Another common form of energy dissipation is Coulomb friction which arises from two surfaces sliding over each other. The friction force is constant but acts in a direction opposite to the direction of the motion. The damping force opposes the motion and will dissipate energy. However, the behaviour is non-linear and Coulomb friction damping cannot be included directly into a linear model. In practice this form of damping is usually linearised by assuming a level of response and using a viscous form of damping. The damping coefficient is found by making the energy dissipation per cycle the same for the Coulomb and the viscous damper. For an assumed harmonic response amplitude $r_0$ with a friction coefficient $\mu$, a normal force F and vibrating at a frequency $\omega$ the equivalent viscous damping coefficient is

$$c_{equiv} = \frac{4\mu F}{\pi \omega r_0}$$

Coulomb damping has a different response characteristic for transient behaviour. If a system with this damping is allowed to vibrate freely then the envelope of the maximum response dies away linearly with time rather than exponentially as it does with viscous damping. Care must be exercised if Coulomb damping is used with a non-linear solution algorithm, especially for one of the various forms of step-by-step integration. Energy is only dissipated if the friction force opposes the motion. If the forces acts in the same direction as the motion then, instead of dissipating energy, it will put energy into the system and cause the amplitude of vibrations to increase. This can easily happen for the higher modes of vibration during a numerically integrated solution causing the process to become numerically unstable. Either a very small integration time step should be used or artificially high viscous damping should be added to the higher modes of vibration.

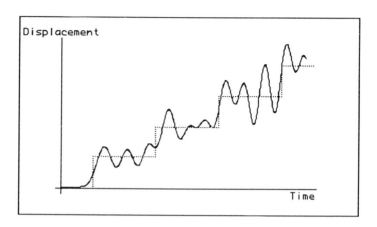

Fig 7.3 Travelling Wave Response

## 7.6 Numerical Damping

The term numerical damping is often encountered, especially when a transient analysis with a impulsive form of input is conducted. In this case the theoretical response with an infinite number of degrees of freedom can show discontinuities in the response. The finite element model, by its very nature, has a finite number of degrees of freedom and this means that it can only model the discontinuous changes in the response in some approximate manner.

A typical finite element displacement response for a pulse travelling down a one dimensional rod is shown in figure 7.3 along with the exact, discontinuous, solution. This is with no damping at all included in the finite element model. It will be seen that there is a considerable amount of 'ringing' within the finite element response where the model tries to fit the sharp transitions in the response as closely as possible. On average the fit is good but obviously at any given time there can be a considerable error. Numerical damping is often used to improve the response in such cases. The numerical damping is not related to any real physical damping, instead its magnitude is chosen to smooth out the response to give a better estimate of the response at any time. The ringing is generally at a high frequency so that this artificial numerical damping is usually chosen to give higher damping for the higher frequencies. If the impulse problem is being solved using some form of time marching step-by-step solution then these schemes often have numerical damping built into them, possibly with a parameter that can be set by the user to control the magnitude of the numerical damping. If a modal solution is being used then there is probably no numerical damping built into the solution scheme. If the user has to explicitly add some artificial numerical damping to control the ringing it is best to use proportional damping of the form $\beta\mathbf{K}$ (see section 7.7.2) since this has a progressively higher damping with frequency. The value of $\beta$, or any numerical damping parameter that is built into the solution scheme has to be chosen by trial and error or by means of past experience. If the numerical damping is too low then there will be considerable ringing in the finite element solution, with large overshoots and undershoots about the correct response. If the numerical damping is too high then the initial part of the response will be correct but as time increases for the response then the numerical damping will progressively smear out the the sharpness of the response and cause the travelling wave motion to be lost. The analyst must decide what is required from the response. If it is only the initial response then a relatively high value of numerical damping can be used. If it is wished to investigate the effect of reflections of the wave off the structures boundaries then a longer response time is implied and a lower value of numerical damping should be used to reduce the progressive smearing effect introduced by the artificial damping. Examples of this are shown in figure 2.6.

## 7.7 Finite Element Modelling of Damping

There are various methods methods currently available in computer systems for modelling damping. Most of these are associated with viscous damping models but some systems have facilities for modelling material damping, usually in the form of a complex Young's modulus. It must be remembered that material damping models are only valid with forcing functions that can be defined in the frequency domain. These are frequency and stationary random responses.

The damping models within systems range in complexity from providing damping finite elements to simple approximations designed to make the mathematical manipulation within the program as simple as possible. The sophistication of the damping model that is available also generally depends upon the solution method being used. The step-by-step integration methods allow any form of viscous damping but eigenvalue methods are usually

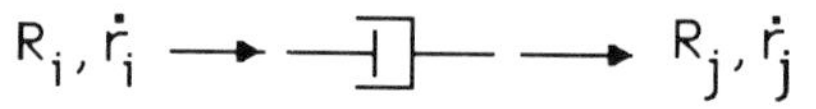

$$R_i, \dot{r}_i \longrightarrow \boxed{\phantom{-}} \longrightarrow R_j, \dot{r}_j$$

$$\begin{bmatrix} R_i \\ R_j \end{bmatrix} = c \begin{bmatrix} 1 & -1 \\ -1 & 1 \end{bmatrix} \begin{bmatrix} \dot{r}_i \\ \dot{r}_j \end{bmatrix}$$

Figure 7.4 - Simple Damping Element

restricted to very simple damping models. This is unfortunate since those forms of problem that are most suited to solution by step-by-step methods are generally not very sensitive to the fine details of the damping distribution. On the other hand the problems that are most amenable to modal solutions are also those that can be sensitive to the distribution of damping. This is especially true if there are any frequencies within the forcing function close to a resonant frequency of the system.

### 7.7.1 Damping Elements

If a specific damping mechanism can be defined then this can be modelled in finite element form in a manner similar to that used for either stiffness or mass elements. The simplest form of damping element is the dashpot as shown in figure 7.4. This element is the damping equivalent of the simple spring element. It can be assembled into a damping matrix in exactly the same way as the stiffness is assembled. More complicated damping elements can also be formed. One that has been used in practice is a radiation damping element, used to model acoustic pressure waves travelling away from the structure.

### 7.7.2 Proportional Damping

One of the most common models of damping provided within a finite element system is proportional damping. In this model no attempt is made to construct damping elements.

Instead the rather arbitrary assumption is made that the damping is a linear combination of the mass and stiffness matrices of the form

$$C = \alpha M + \beta K$$

There is no real physical justification for this although the $\alpha M$ term vaguely represents radiation damping from thin plates and the $\beta K$ term similarly is a crude approximation to structural damping in some instances. In reality this assumption is made purely for mathematical convenience as it simplifies the solution process. The values for $\alpha$ and $\beta$ are chosen to give the correct order of magnitude for the damping at two frequencies. If the required damping ratio at the frequency $\omega_r$ is $\zeta_r$ and at the frequency $\omega_s$ it is $\zeta_s$ then the values for $\alpha$ and $\beta$ are given by

$$\alpha = 2\omega_r\omega_s \, (\zeta_s\omega_r - \zeta_r\omega_s)/(\omega_r^2 - \omega_s^2)$$

$$\beta = 2 \, (\zeta_r\omega_r - \zeta_s\omega_s)/(\omega_r^2 - \omega_s^2)$$

For the special case of $\zeta_r = \zeta_s$ the resulting variation of damping with frequency is shown in figure 7.5b. Note that the damping is less than the specified value between the two frequencies $\omega_r$ and $\omega_s$ and it is greater than the specified value out of this range. It rises rapidly outside the specified frequency range. The model cannot be physically correct since it gives infinite damping at zero frequency. The damping at frequencies below $\omega_r$ is largely controlled by the mass part of the assumption and above $\omega_s$ it is largely controlled by the stiffness.

Although the assumption of proportional damping has no real physical basis, in practice the damping distribution is rarely known in sufficient detail to warrant any other more complicated model. Proportional damping will serve to give each mode of vibration the correct order of magnitude of damping and, provided that the component of the response of interest is not controlled by the damping, it is often sufficient. It ceases to be reliable when the damping within the system becomes significant, say above 10% of critical, or where the damping is concentrated within a small region of the structure. This is especially the case if some damping has been included in the structure with the specific purpose of controlling the dynamic response.

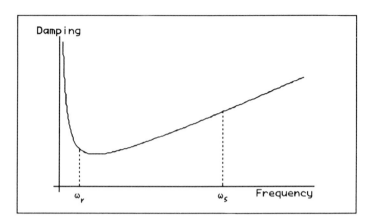

<u>Figure 7.5a - Proportional Damping with $\zeta_s > \zeta_r$</u>

Figure 7.5a shows how the damping factor for proportional damping varies with frequency when $\zeta_s$ is greater than $\zeta_r$. In this case it is seen that the damping increases rapidly with

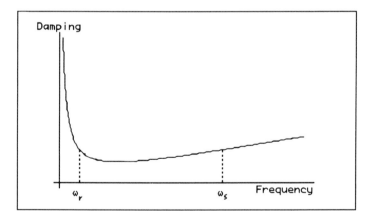

<u>Figure 7.5b - Proportional Damping with $\zeta_s = \zeta_r$</u>

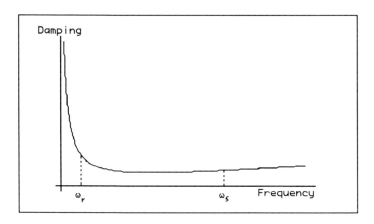

Figure 7.5c - Proportional Damping with $\zeta_s < \zeta_r$

frequency. This assumption is often used when proportional damping is being employed to provide numerical damping since it gives rise to higher damping in the less accurate higher modes.

Figure 7.5c illustrates the variation of the damping when $\zeta_r$ is greater than $\zeta_s$. In this case the high frequency damping does not rise so rapidly but it does, nevertheless, still increase.

### 7.7.3 Modal Damping

Another approximate form of damping model that is often available within finite element systems is modal damping. This form of damping is only applicable if a modal solution involving the systems eigenvectors is being conducted. The eigenvalues and eigenvectors (resonant frequencies and mode shapes) are found for the undamped system and used to transform the equations to their modal form. Typically for the j'th mode this is

$$\ddot{q}_j + \omega_j^2 q_j = Q_j$$

At this stage a modal damping coefficient is added to include the effect of damping so that the modal equation becomes

$$\ddot{q}_j + 2\zeta_j\omega_j\dot{q}_j + \omega_j^2 q_j = Q_j$$

where $\zeta_j$ is the modal damping value. Generally this is obtained by experiment.

Modal damping gives a rather more precise model for the damping within the system provided that the modal damping factors, $\zeta_j$, are known. If not it is little better than the proportional damping assumption. In fact, it can be shown that the proportional damping assumption is just the first two terms in a series and if all of the terms are taken then the modal damping values are recovered. If the damping values are known accurately from an experiment on the structure this provides a good damping model.

## 7.8 Damping Within Structures

Within real structures there are possibilities of various forms of energy dissipation mechanisms. It can be built into the structure specifically to control the amplitude of the dynamic response or it can arise from less specific causes. If there is no built in damping then the energy can be dissipated by the material composing the structure or by the surrounding medium.

### 7.8.1 Experimental Damping Measurements

If the damping is found from experimental measurements then care must be taken in interpreting the results of such measurements, especially where the damping is light. If care is not taken the damping can be more a function of the environment, the support system, the excitation and measuring attachments. Similarly, the damping of the structure when it is in situ can be largely determined by its environment rather than the damping inherent within the structure. The most realistic measurements of damping are likely to be obtained by measurements taken on the structure under operating conditions. This is rarely possible, certainly not at the design stage, and the next best thing is to use the measured damping values of similar structures.

## 7.8.2 Material Damping

Internal energy dissipation within the material itself is often quoted (usually in terms of loss factors or a complex Young's modulus) for engineering materials. These figures should be treated with caution. If the material damping of metals is measured in carefully controlled conditions, where the effects of the environment has been excluded as far as is possible, the material damping is found to be very low, considerably less than 1% of critical.

## 7.8.3 Radiation Damping

Probably the major natural mechanism for damping structures is from radiation damping. If a plate vibrates in a fluid then sound waves radiate from it. As these waves travel away from the plate then progressively more of the fluid is set into motion. The energy is transferred from the structure to the fluid so that, as far as the structure is concerned, it is losing energy. If a plane wave is considered then the energy transferred per unit area per cycle is

$$E = \pi \omega \rho c r^2$$

where $\rho$ is the density of the medium transmitting the wave, c the speed of sound in this medium and r is the amplitude of vibration. The energy dissipated per cycle is the same as that for a viscous damper with a damping coefficient of $\rho c$ per unit area. This is called the characteristic impedance of the medium.

Even with a low density medium, such as air, this gives a very significant contribution to the damping within the structure. If the structure is surrounded by a denser medium such as water then radiation damping is very significant. If a structure is built into a solid foundation or support then the radiation damping into the foundation can give a relatively high damping value at the connection point. In civil engineering structures this is the major component of foundation damping. To illustrate the importance of this an undamped model of a framed structure was modelled including its foundations. The radiation into the foundation gave the structure an apparent damping factor 10% of critical. A second study took measured damping values for piles in a river bed and tested various damping models against these values. The models included radiation damping into the foundation, material damping in the piles, drag from the river current and a viscous mud model for the river bed. The only mechanism that gave a realistic representation of the measured damping was the radiation damping. All of the other mechanisms gave damping values an order of magnitude less.

### 7.8.4 Damping at Joints

Another source of damping within structures is associated with the joints of the structure. This is both difficult to quantify and to model. A bolted or riveted joint can dissipated energy in two ways. The surfaces of the joint can slide over each other and give rise to Coulomb friction. Alternatively the faces of the joint can move normal to each other so that for a large part of each vibration cycle the faces are not in contact. This can cause air or any other fluid surrounding the structure to be pumped in and out of the joint and this causes energy dissipation.

The ill defined nature of joint damping, together with the fact that it arises locally at various points or lines within the structure makes it very difficult to model. This is true for finite element models also. The finite element method smears the effects over the element and the local details associated with the edge of the element, typical of joint damping, are not easily included. The effect of joint damping is almost invariably included in terms of the level of modal damping factors chosen for the model rather than as explicit features of the idealisation.

### 7.8.5 Differing Damping Levels in Various Parts of the Structure

If a structure is composed of more than one material, or there are different fabrication methods used in different parts of the structure, then these different areas can have different damping values. If the damping is being modelled in great detail in terms of damping elements then this presents no problem. However, if either proportional or modal damping is being used then these simplifications almost invariably have the effect of smearing the damping over the complete structure and ceasing to differentiate between the different parts.

This is probably realistic if all parts of the structure are responding to the same order of magnitude but the same effect can be achieved by using an average damping (or for a conservative calculation the lowest) damping factor for the complete model.

If modal damping is being used, rather than proportional damping, then it becomes possible to be more precise over the assumed damping. The undamped modes of vibration can be found and inspected. If the large motion response of a mode is restricted to one area associated with a single damping value then this can be used as the modal damping factor for that mode. If the mode involves significant response in areas where more than one damping value is valid then an average factor can be used for that mode.

## 7.9 The Importance of Damping

One theme that is apparent in the preceding sections is that, for most structural problems, the damping is small, ill defined and difficult to model accurately. One question that then arises is 'how important is it to specify the damping accurately?' The answer to this question depends upon various factors but mainly upon the type of forcing function, the level of damping and whether the damping is being used to control (either directly or indirectly) the dynamic response.

### 7.9.1 The Consequences of the Forcing Function

If the applied forcing function is essentially impulsive in nature, that is it is a short duration transient, then, provided that the damping is light, it has relatively little effect upon the response and only the order of magnitude of the damping need be defined. Proportional damping is normally sufficient, often with $\alpha=0$ so that the damping is low for the low frequency response but increases with increasing frequency. This will tend to give a conservative solution since the main response effects tend to be associated with the low frequency behaviour. Also the finite element idealisation becomes increasingly less accurate with increasing frequency so that this form of damping, proportional to stiffness only, will tend to de-emphasise the more approximate part of the response.

If the force input is periodic and the steady state response is required then a better knowledge of the damping values might be needed. If the forcing function does not contain any frequency component near to a resonant frequency then the precise damping value is not necessary. In this case simple proportional damping is sufficient. If there are some frequency components in the input close to a resonance then it becomes more important to define the damping for the modes that are being excited near to resonance. The closer the excitation is to a resonance then the more important it is to specify the damping accurately. If the excitation is exactly on a resonance then the response in this mode is controlled entirely by the damping. In practice this is not a realistic case since a better design solution is not to try to specify the damping very precisely but to modify the structure slightly to separate the resonance from the excitation frequency. The only time that this is not possible is for random excitation which contains all frequencies and the resonances will always be excited. The mean square response of the structure is then largely dominated by the response around each resonance and reasonably accurate damping values are required in this case. For random response the accuracy of the response calculation will be of the same degree of accuracy to which the damping is specified. There are also other circumstances in which it is not possible to modify the structural behaviour. Typically, the running up of a rotating machine can pass through critical frequencies no matter how the structure is modified. A turbine with many discs each having many blades will have so many resonant frequencies that at least one will be difficult to avoid. In some such cases the start up and operating conditions must be carefully controlled.

*7.9.2 The Level of Damping*

For a lightly damped system it must be recognised that it is very unlikely that a precise damping value can be obtained. In many cases where the damping is light the nature of the forcing function is such that the damping need only be specified to an order of magnitude, with the structure being designed to avoid any near resonance response. In this case the damping need not be given with precision and the lowest estimate for the damping should be used to give a conservative design. In many cases it is sufficient to assume no damping at all. If the excitation is near to a resonance then a realistic damping factor for that mode should be given. For most analyses where the damping is not accurately known then the best strategy is to choose a form of damping that underestimates the damping values for the low frequency response but overestimates for the high frequency components. This will be consistent with the finite element idealisation where the model reproduces the low frequency behaviour accurately but has an increasing error associated with the higher frequency idealisation.

For higher damping levels the response will become a function of damping over all of the frequency range. However, the higher damping must be coming from some mechanism and this should be identified and modelled. If the estimated damping is more than 20% of critical then the use of proportional damping models or even modal damping factors should be avoided. In this case the damping mechanism must be identified and modelled explicitly as damping elements. This is because the simple models such as proportional damping tend to smear the damping equally into all of the modes. As the damping becomes higher and it is associated with an identifiable energy dissipation mechanism then it is found that the damping is not equally distributed in all of the modes. Instead some modes become highly damped whilst other modes, that do not excite the damping mechanism, have a low damping. This range of damping values within the modes makes the use of an average high level of damping for all of the modes dangerous and unrealistic.

In general terms damping values less than 10% of critical can usually be handled by simple proportional damping or constant modal damping factor models with the lower values for the estimated damping being used. If the damping is greater than 20% of critical then the mechanism giving rise to the damping must be identified and modelled using damping elements to form a damping matrix. If this cannot be done then a much lower damping value must be assumed. If the damping is between 10 to 20% of critical then the effect of varying the damping on the response should be investigated. If the response is not very sensitive to the damping value simple damping models can be used. If the response is sensitive a more detailed damping model must be constructed and a damping matrix formed.

### 7.9.3 Controlling Response with Damping

In some circumstances damping is specifically built into the structure to control the vibration levels or otherwise modify the dynamic response. In such cases the damping

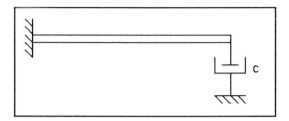

Figure 7.6 - Beam with Damping

must be modelled in detail since the smearing effect of simple damping models can lead to false conclusions. To illustrate this consider the simple cantilever beam shown in figure 7.6. In this illustration a dashpot, c, has been added to the tip of the cantilever to control the response. If the damping value is increased then the level of the tip response will decrease. If the damping is made very high then the tip response will tend to zero. However, this does not mean that the response in the centre of the beam will decrease. What will happen in fact is that, as the damping is increased, the tip response will be reduced as if a support is added at the tip. The behaviour for a large value of the damping, c, will be exactly the same as for a lightly damped propped cantilever. As the damping is increased then the nature of the mode shapes will change from those of a simple cantilever to those of a propped cantilever. If proportional damping is used and the damping is increased to a large value then a totally different behaviour will be observed. In this case the response in all of the modes will decrease and the nature of the mode shapes will not alter with the level of damping

## 7.10  Special Damping Considerations

There are some dynamics problems where damping can play a special role in the form of response. Two examples of this are wave propagation into an infinite (or very large) region and aeroelastic problems.

### 7.10.1 Wave Propagation and Radiation Damping

The effect of the medium surrounding a structure on the damping of the structure has been discussed in a previous section. As the structure vibrates it generates waves into the surrounding medium. There can be a special case of this where the total structure is very large in size compared to the area of interest, typically a building resting on the ground. This makes the foundation very large with respect to the size of the structure. With a finite element model that includes the foundation the analyst must choose to terminate the mesh in the foundation, thereby introducing an artificial boundary into the problem. As the structure vibrates it will generate pressure waves into the foundation. These will reflect off the artificial boundaries back to the structure, thereby altering its dynamic response. In reality the boundaries are not there and the waves will not be reflected back to the structure. To model the real problem using finite elements the artificial boundaries must be made to absorb the pressure waves to prevent reflection. One method of doing this is to place distributed damping elements around the boundary with a damping coefficient of $\rho c$ per unit area, where $\rho$ is the density of the foundation and c is the velocity of a normal pressure wave for dampers normal to the to the boundary and the shear wave velocity for dampers tangential to the boundary. Provided that the boundary is sufficiently far from the structure that the radiated waves have become plane then this forms a good representation of a non-reflecting boundary.

### 7.10.2 Aeroelasticity

If a flexible structure is immersed in a fluid that is flowing past it then there is a possibility of the two interacting dynamically to produce the aeroelastic effect known as flutter. In effect the aerodynamic, structural and inertia forces interact in this case to such an extent that the effective damping of the system in one or more modes becomes negative. This means that the structure is extracting energy from the air(fluid) stream and transforming this into vibrational energy. The amplitude of vibrations then grow rapidly to a very large value, often leading to structural failure. This will occur above some critical fluid velocity known as the flutter speed. To solve such a problem both the fluid and the structural effects must be included in the model. This leads to a set of equations similar to those for arbitrary viscous damping and their solution, together with how the onset of the dynamic instability is detected, is discussed in the next section. Most flutter problems require the presence of two or more structural resonances that become coupled together by the aerodynamic forces. This is known as binary flutter. Typically the bending and torsion modes of an aircraft wing interact with the airflow to produce classical wing flutter.

If a structure is undamped this does not mean that flutter will occur at any fluid velocity. The interaction causing flutter is quite complex and requires that the amplitude and the phases of the various force components combine in a special manner such that the airflow does positive work on the structure over a cycle of vibration. Energy is taken from the airflow since it is assumed that this always flows with the same velocity. This will only be the case above a critical fluid velocity, even for an undamped system.The frequency at which flutter occurs will not be a structural resonance, but it will be an eigenvalue of the combined fluid/structure system of equations. The solution to this eigenvalue problem yields both the flutter frequency and the flutter airflow velocity. Damping tends to raise the flutter speed but, for a conservative estimate, then the structural damping can be (and usually is) ignored.

Flutter, or its equivalent, can occur whenever there is an interaction between coupled problems where one of the components of the system is transporting energy. This is typified by aeroelasticity where the energy to sustain the flutter vibrations comes from the air flow. Flutter has caused structural failures in such diverse situations as aircraft, suspension bridges and power cable vibrations. When it occurs it usually leads to a rapid structural failure and must be avoided. It is difficult to cure. The structure can be stiffened to increase the flutter speed but this adds mass which has the opposite effect. Better techniques involve trying to minimise the coupling between the fluid and the structure and the individual modes in the structure. Typically, for the classic wing flutter the structure is modified, possibly by adding mass, to make the shear centre and the centre of gravity of the wing cross-section to coincide. This removes one coupling component and flutter cannot occur. Similarly for control surfaces, these are mass balanced by adding mass to make the centre of gravity of the control surface coincide with the hinge line. For non-aerodynamic structures the external shape of the structure can be changed to remove the aerodynamic coupling.

## 7.11 Solution Methods and Damping

Most finite element programs have solution techniques that are restricted to the simple damping models. Almost all are limited to viscous damping with no material (or hysteretic) damping models. This is not too restrictive since the material damping model is only valid for a periodic response, even when it is expressed in its complex stiffness form without the frequency appearing explicitly. When the damping within a finite element system is only viscous it is often restricted to proportional or modal damping models. Proportional damping is satisfactory for the usual case where the damping is less than 10% of critical, where the damping is not well defined and where the response is not too sensitive to the damping. In other circumstances more detail is required within the damping model. Unfortunately, this is not just a case of including damping elements within the system, since the conventional dynamic solution techniques usually have to be changed to incorporate the refined damping models.

If a step-by-step time domain solution is being used then these can often accommodate a completely general viscous damping matrix. Unfortunately the types of problems where the damping is important are long duration steady state response problems which are not well suited to time domain step-by-step solutions. One exception to this is where damping is used to model radiation damping boundary conditions. This is directly relevant to to wave propagation, impact, type of problems. The damping matrix for the boundary damping must be formed to model this effect correctly, it cannot be approximated by modal damping or proportional damping. In other circumstances, where an essentially steady state response is required, then other solution methods are normally used for the sake of efficiency.

The modal solution method requires considerable modification to include arbitrary damping. Proportional damping is convenient mathematically because it can be shown in this case that the damped modal coordinates are identical to the undamped ones. Similarly, for modal damping, the undamped modal coordinates are used to uncouple the equations of motion. However, for arbitrary viscous damping employing a damping matrix that has been constructed from damping elements or for a model using proportional damping where different constants $\alpha$ and $\beta$ are used in different parts of the model, then the damped normal coordinates must be found by solving the damped eigenvalue problem. The equation of motion with arbitrary viscous damping is

$$M\ddot{r} + C\dot{r} + Kr = R(t)$$

To find the damped normal modes an auxiliary equation

$$M\dot{r} - M\dot{r} = 0$$

is also used. Combining these together gives the equation set

$$\begin{bmatrix} 0 & M \\ M & C \end{bmatrix} \begin{bmatrix} \ddot{r} \\ \dot{r} \end{bmatrix} + \begin{bmatrix} -M & 0 \\ 0 & K \end{bmatrix} \begin{bmatrix} \dot{r} \\ r \end{bmatrix} = \begin{bmatrix} 0 \\ R(t) \end{bmatrix}$$

and this gives the damped eigenvalue problem that has to be solved. In this case the total coefficient matrices are symmetric but they are not positive definite and the resulting eigenvalues and eigenvectors are complex numbers. The imaginary part of the eigenvalues give the damped resonant frequencies and the real part gives the damping component. The real part should always be negative for the damping to dissipate energy. If the real part is positive then energy is being fed into the system and it is unstable. Typically, for aeroelastic flutter problems the equations are set up for various air speeds and the damped eigenvalues found. If any eigenvalue has a positive real coefficient then the system is unstable and flutter will occur at that air speed.

If the damping in any mode is above critical then the corresponding eigenvalue will be a real negative number with no imaginary part. For structures with viscous damping the complex eigenvalues will either be real or occur as complex conjugate pairs. If an eigenvalue is complex then the eigenvector will also consist of complex numbers. Again the eigenvectors occur as complex conjugate pairs. The real and imaginary parts of the eigenvectors can be interpreted as the different points on the structure being out of phase with each other. The real part of a term in the eigenvector gives the in phase component of that displacement and the imaginary part the out of phase component. The eigenvectors cannot be found absolutely, the terms in any eigenvector can only be found relative to each other. This is true for both undamped and damped eigenvectors. In practice this means that the values within an eigenvector can all be multiplied by an arbitrary complex number and it is still a valid eigenvector. This can make comparison of damped eigenvectors between analysis systems very difficult but they can each be correct. There is no ambiguity about the eigenvalue since these are determined absolutely and should be identical between different computer programs for the same model. Note that the eigenvalues can be complex but the eigenvectors completely real. This will, in fact, be the case for systems with proportional or modal damping. In such cases the damped and undamped eigenvectors are identical.

If a damped modal solution is used then it transpires that the solution solves for the displacements and the velocities independently. The velocities can also be found by differentiating the displacements with respect to time. These two methods for finding the velocities of a damped system should obviously lead to identical results. It can be shown that this is only the case if all of the damped eigenvectors are used in the damped modal solution. Modal truncation of the damped modes leads to inconsistent results for the velocities and it is not possible to say which is correct. To overcome this difficulty the required number of undamped modes should first be determined and then these used to condense the damped equations to a set of this small size. All of the damped eigenvalues and eigenvectors of this condensed set are found and used in the response calculation. This will make the velocities consistent no matter how they are calculated. It will also mean that the calculation of the damped modes only takes place on a small set of equations and this reduces the numerical complexity of finding the damped eigenvalues and vectors considerably. The small set can be held in the computer's fast memory and the QR algorithm used to determine the eigenvalues and vectors.

It is possible to set up the damped eigenvalue problem including both viscous and material damping. This is derived from a set of dynamic equations of the form:

$$\begin{bmatrix} 0 & M \\ M & C \end{bmatrix} \begin{bmatrix} \ddot{r} \\ \dot{r} \end{bmatrix} + \begin{bmatrix} -M & 0 \\ 0 & K+iH \end{bmatrix} \begin{bmatrix} \dot{r} \\ r \end{bmatrix} = \begin{bmatrix} 0 \\ R(t) \end{bmatrix}$$

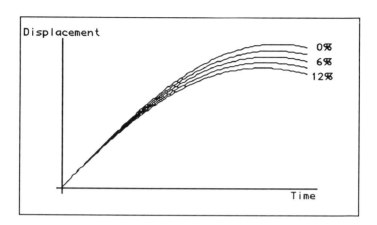

Fig 7.7 - Short Term Time Response with Different Damping Levels

where **H** is the material damping matrix. In this case the equations are complex but they can be solved in the usual way merely by using complex arithmetic in the eigenvalue algorithm. However, when the eigenvalues are computed they are found to be complex numbers and do not occur as complex conjugate pairs. Further, it is found that the real part of some of

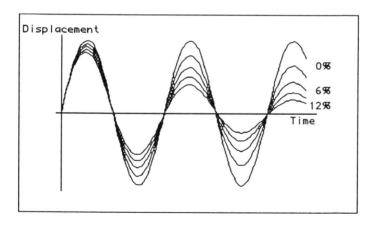

Fig 7.8 - Long Term Time Response with Different Damping Levels

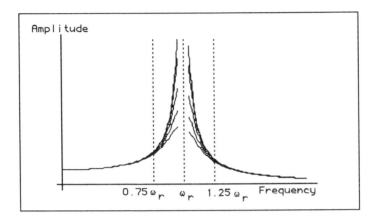

Fig 7.9 Variation of Steady State Response with Damping

the complex eigenvalues are positive, implying that the system is unstable. This is a direct consequence of the idealisation that was made in assuming that the material damping was independent of frequency. In reality this is only a linearisation to represent the hysteresis loop and is not physically meaningful unless a frequency is defined.

The material damping model using a complex stiffness should not be used in a general response calculation since it leads to nonsensical results. It is valid if the response is restricted to a steady state harmonic excitation.

| Damping Factor | $\dfrac{\text{Peak Displacement}}{\text{Zero Damping Peak Displacement}}$ |
|:---:|:---:|
| 0 | 1.000 |
| 0.03 | 0.954 |
| 0.06 | 0.912 |
| 0.09 | 0.872 |
| 0.12 | 0.833 |

Table 7.1 - Variation of Peak Impulse Response with Damping

## 7.12 The Effect of Damping Upon the Response

In many cases the damping is so small that it has little effect upon the response and only a rough estimate of it is required. The effect of damping on a transient response is shown in figures 7.7 and 7.8. Figure 7.7 shows in detail the peak response of a single degree of freedom system arising from an impulsive load. The damping factor is varied from zero to 12% but there is only a relatively small change in the maximum amplitude of the response. The actual reduction in amplitude compared to the zero damping case is given in table 7.1. The damping does have a significant effect upon the long term response, as shown in figure 7.8. If it is required to find the long term response accurately then care must be taken over the choice of damping factor. If only the peak response is required then it is most conservative to use zero damping since such a conservatism is not very high and will not lead to a considerable increase in the peak response. The damping value is also not critical in many cases of steady state response. Figure 7.9 shows the steady state response of a single degree of freedom system again for damping values between zero and 12% of critical. The response at the resonant frequency, $\omega_r$, is not plotted since the zero damping case has an infinite response at this frequency. It will be seen that, close to the resonance the damping is very important but for excitation frequencies less than 0.75 $\omega_r$ or greater than 1.25 $\omega_r$ then the response is not affected by the damping and a zero value can be used.

# CHAPTER 8 - RESULTS INTERPRETATION AND PRESENTATION

## 8.1 Introduction

Any dynamic analysis can produce vast quantities of output and the user must give careful consideration to what he requests to be printed. The possible volume of output can be appreciated by considering a time history solution with, say, a thousand response steps calculated. The output for each step would typically consist of the displacements, the velocities and the accelerations at the nodes in addition to the stresses. Assuming 1000 nodes with two lines of output for each node this give two million lines of output or some thirty thousand pages of paper. Such a volume of data is impossible to digest and only a small percentage of it is actually of interest to the analyst. The problem with dynamics is that it is difficult to estimate beforehand which parts of the output are actually of interest.

Obviously a graphical presentation of the data conveys the results in a more digestible form but even this can produce a very large volume of output. If all of the results for the example cited above are plotted then it would require some 4000 plots. This is still such a large figure as to be impractical for everyday use. A large volume of data also presents problems when interacting with post-processors that allow graphical manipulation of the results. For the typical example cited above this would involve a data transfer of somewhere between 6 million to 12 million numbers, that is 24 to 48 million bytes of data.

The freedom that a user has to obtain edited forms of the results depends upon the type of analysis that is being conducted and the facilities within the program that is being used. If the system allows easy restarting at any stage then the user can control the volume of output by initially generating a small amount of output to indicate where in time and space the significant results occur. More detailed output can then be obtained at these points by restarting the analysis. The assessment of the significant points in time and space is easiest if a modal solution is being used and requires rather more judgment and experience on the part of the analyst for direct solutions.

## 8.2 The Required Results

The results that a user requires obviously depends upon the analysis in hand. They generally include some combination of the following quantities:

a.  Resonant frequencies.

b.  Mode shapes.

c.  Time histories of displacements, velocities and accelerations.

d.  Time histories of stresses, internal forces and reactions.

e.  Frequency response of the structure in terms of displacements, velocities and accelerations.

f.  Frequency response of stresses, internal forces and reactions.

g.  Response spectrum of a point to be used as data for a subsequent dynamic analysis.

h.  The maximum displacement, velocity and acceleration at each node at any time or frequency.

i.  The maximum stress, internal force or reaction at any time or frequency.

j.  Spectral density of the displacements, velocities and accelerations.

k.  The spectral density of the stresses, internal forces and reactions.

l.  The root mean square response of the displacements, velocities and accelerations.

m.  The root mean square response of the stresses.

Items a and b are obtained from an eigenvalue analysis and items h and i can be obtained from any forced response calculation. Items c, d and g are obtained from a time domain response using either a modal or a direct integration solution. Items e and f are obtained from a frequency domain response using either a modal or a dynamic stiffness solution. A response spectrum analysis will generate items h and i and a random response analysis will give items j to m.

If one object of the analysis is to correlate with experimental data then it is likely that other items of data will be required. Quantities that can be readily measured are resonant frequencies and mode shapes, mobilities and spectral densities. The results that are required are well defined in this case since they must correspond to the experimental results. It is also possible that other items of data can be required for a detailed comparison between experiment and theory, typically the stiffness and mass matrices condensed to the experimental measurement points.

## 8.3 Overall Checks

As with any finite element analysis within dynamics it is important to check the basic features of the analysis before the results are interpreted. One set of checks is associated with the mass of the structure. The finite element system should provide facilities for using the mass matrix to determine the total mass of the structure, the position of the centre of gravity and the moments of inertia about the centre of gravity. The total structural volume should also be printed if its density varies within the structure. Such quantities as the total mass and total volume are usually known for other reasons and provide a good basic first check on the model  It can also be convenient to have the mass and volume of each element available since this allows any discrepancy between the mass of the finite element model and the real mass of the structure to be isolated to a group of elements if there is a local error.

The position of the centre of gravity and the moments of inertia are more difficult to check but they can be useful where mass lumping, a Guyan reduction or substructuring has been used. The mass quantities are computed for the full model and then re-computed for the Guyan reduced mass or the final substructure mass. They should be the same at this stage as they were before any reduction was made. If they are not then the reduction process has altered the global mass characteristics and the solution will be in error.

Another very good check to carry out if Guyan reduction or dynamic substructuring has been used is to confirm that the reduced stiffness matrix has the same number of rigid body modes after the reduction as there was before. If there is not then the resulting reduced equations are wrong and should be discarded.

## 8.4 Output from an Eigenvalue Analysis

An eigenvalue analysis calculates the eigenvalues and eigenvectors by solving the equation

$$K\phi_i = \lambda_i M\phi_i \qquad\qquad 8.1$$

where $\lambda_i$ is the i'th eigenvalue and $\phi_i$ the corresponding vector. The square root of the eigenvalue is the resonant frequency in radians per second, which is easily converted into Hz or the period of oscillation of the mode. Most systems provide a table of the computed eigenvalues in one or more of these forms.

Each eigenvalue has an eigenvector (or mode shape) associated with it and this can be presented in tabular or graphical form. It will be seen from equation 8.1 that the eigenvector, $\phi_i$, can be multiplied by an arbitrary scalar but the equation is still correct. This means that the eigenvector cannot be specified absolutely but can only be given in terms of relative amplitudes. So far as presenting the vectors are concerned this leads to various alternative possible tabulated values, all of which are correct but which produce apparently different vectors since they have a different scaling. The process of scaling the vector is called normalisation. The usual forms of normalisation are:

a.  No specific normalisation, the vector is printed as computed.

b.  An engineering normalisation, where the vector is scaled so that the largest term is unity. This is the best form for printing the vectors since the user can assess the relative importance of any term in the eigenvector knowing that the largest value is unity. This is sometimes modified for beams, plates and shells, where rotations, occur so that the normalisation is only carried out on the translational displacements. The relative values of displacements and rotations involve a length quantity and hence the magnitude of the rotations depend upon the units used for the analysis.

c.  A mathematical normalisation, where the vector is scaled such that $\phi_i^t M\phi_i = 1$. Modal response calculations involve divisions by this quantity and become trivial with such a normalisation. A restricted form of this is to normalise the vector such that $\phi_i{}^t\phi_i = 1$. This arises from a special form of the eigenvalue problem and has little relevance for a dynamic analysis.

Probably the best compromise is to display the eigenvectors using the engineering normalisation (b), but to store them internally using the mathematical normalisation, (c). If the eigenvectors are being saved for subsequent use external to the analysis program the user must confirm in which form the eigenvectors have been normalised before using them. Almost invariably the mathematical normalisation is the most useful.

Another quantity that is often printed out with the eigenvalue or eigenvector is the modal mass (or generalised mass). This is the product $\phi_i{}^tM\phi_i$. If the mathematical normalisation is used it will be unity. The value of the modal mass should be that for the vector $\phi_i$ as printed in order for it to have relevance. The magnitude of the modal mass has no physical significance since it can be made any value by altering the normalisation of the eigenvector. The relative values of modal masses between modes also have no physical significance. A low value of modal mass in mode A and a high value in mode B cannot be interpreted to imply that mode A is unimportant with respect to mode B or that more of the structure mass is associated with mode B. The modal mass is only given so that the analyst can carry out further response calculations using the printed eigenvector, external to the analysis program.

The corresponding modal (or generalised stiffness) $\phi_i{}^tK\phi_i$ is also printed by some programs. Again this has no physical meaning and cannot be used for interpreting the results. However, the ratio of the modal stiffness to the modal mass is the eigenvalue $\lambda_j$. This is independent of the normalisation used. For mathematical normalisation the modal stiffness is the eigenvalue.

The arbitrary nature of the normalisation means that the user should take care when comparing tables of mode shapes printed by different programs. If alternative normalisations have been used then the printed values can look very different although the relative shapes are the same. Some care must also be exercised even when the same normalisation method has been used since a factor of -1 can still be applied between the vectors, giving them different signs. Sometimes this can cause confusion since a slight

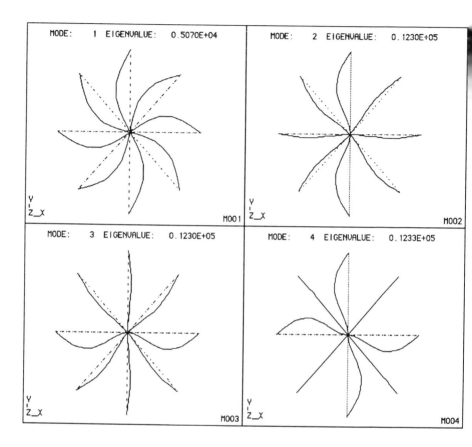

Fig 8.1a - Mode Shapes for Multiple Eigenvalues (Modes 1 to 4)

change in the geometry can then cause some vectors to change sign. It can also cause plots of mode shapes to look different, especially for the higher, more complicated, modes.

## 8.5 Symmetric Structures

If the geometry of the structure is symmetric about a plane then half of the modes will also be symmetric in shape about this plane. The other half of the modes will be anti symmetric. This can often be used to test the accuracy of the computed mode. If the geometry is

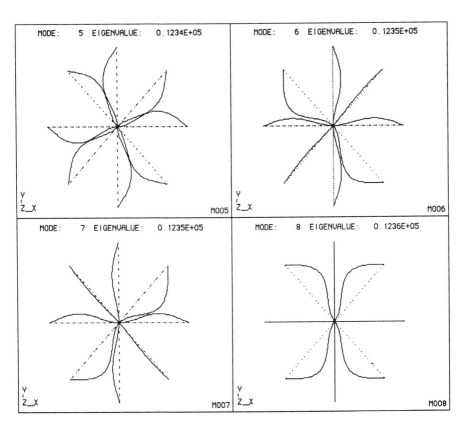

Fig 8.1b - Mode Shapes for Multiple Eigenvalues (Modes 5 to 8)

symmetric then the modes must be either symmetric or anti symmetric, except for the special case of multiple eigenvalues discussed in the next section. If they are not it indicates an error. Other forms of symmetry, typically cyclic symmetry, have similar properties of allowing the modes to be grouped into classes defined by the geometrical symmetry. The more symmetries that a structure has the more chance there is of multiple eigenvalues occuring. However, the presence of geometrical symmetries does not imply that there will be multiple eigenvalues since this does depend upon the precise nature of the mass and stiffness distributions within the structure.

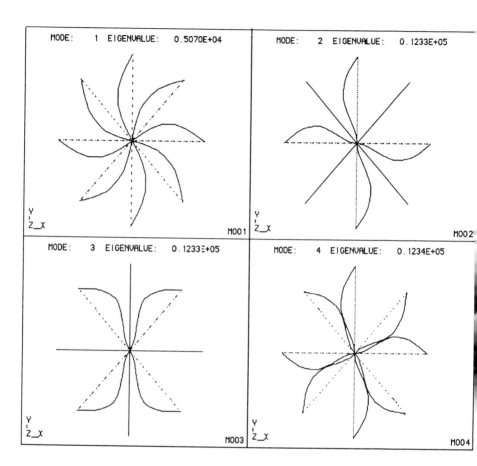

Fig 8.2a - Alternative Mode Shapes for Multiple Eigenvalues (Modes 1 to 4)

## 8.6 Multiple Eigenvalues

In some instances a structure can have more than one eigenvalue with the same numerical value. An unsupported, three dimensional structure will have six zero (rigid body) eigenvalues. Structures that are symmetric about one or more planes often have two or more equal eigenvalues. If a structure has two equal eigenvalues then it can be shown that the two corresponding eigenvectors are not unique. Given any two independent vectors that

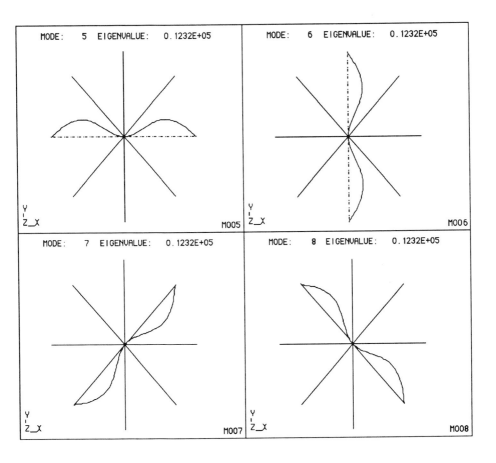

Fig 8.2b - Alternative Mode Shapes for Multiple Eigenvalues (Modes 5 to 8)

satisfy the eigenvalue equation for the multiple eigenvalue then any linear combination of these two vectors also satisfy the equation. That is if

$$K\phi_i = \lambda M\phi_i \quad \text{and} \quad K\phi_j = \lambda M\phi_j \quad \text{where} \quad \lambda = \lambda_i = \lambda_j$$

then

$$K(a\phi_i + b\phi_j) = \lambda M (a\phi_i + b\phi_j)$$

for any value of a or b. This is illustrated in figures 8.1 and 8.2 The mode shapes of the first eight modes of one of the NAFEMS dynamic test bench marks are plotted here. Both sets are correct although some modes look very different. The modes of figure 8.2 are in fact linear combinations of the modes of figure 8.1 The first mode shape is a single mode and has the same mode shape in both cases. Modes 2 to 4 in figure 8.2a shows that three of the modes can be represented by two of the beams vibrating antisymmetrically such that no external moment is induced at the centre of the structure. If only one beam vibrated in this way, with zero slope at the centre, an external moment would be required for equilibrium. If two identical beams vibrate in opposite directions then they balance each other. Note that although mode 1 involves antisymmetric bending of all of the beams their slope at the centre is not zero and so no external moment is needed. The modes 2 to 4 in figure 8.2 occur exactly as modes 4, 8 and 5 respectively of figure 8.1. The modes in figure 8.2b are all symmetric vibration of each component beam in turn. The axial stiffness of the beam is so high compared to the bending stiffness that they act as props to these modes. The corresponding modes occur as linear combinations of these separate movements in figure 8.1. This means that there is no unique set of vectors and it can sometimes be difficult to categorise the eigenvectors corresponding to multiple eigenvalues. It also means that it is quite possible for different systems to obtain two apparently different eigenvectors.

Provided that one set can be obtained as linear combinations of the other then they are both correct. To test for correspondence it is necessary to investigate such linear combinations. For rigid body motions it is probably easiest for the user to think in terms of rigid body translations parallel to the global axes and rigid body rotations about the centre of gravity. For symmetric geometries it is natural to think in terms of symmetric and anti-symmetric modes. Most systems do not present results in this form for multiple eigenvalues but they can still be completely correct. Isolated eigenvalues always have a unique eigenvector associated with them.

## 8.7 Checking Eigenvalues and Eigenvectors

It is difficult to check the eigenvalues of anything other than simple structures. The eigenvectors will generally become more complicated in shape the higher the mode number, but this can be obscured to some extent if the modes are sequences of local and global modes. The eigenvectors can be tested numerically by forming the products $\phi_i{}^t M\phi_j$ and comparing this with the minimum of either $\phi_i{}^t M\phi_i$ or $\phi_j{}^t M\phi_j$. If $\phi_i{}^t M\phi_j$ is less than $10^{-6}$ times the minimum of these then orthogonality is satisfied. If it is comparable to or greater than the minimum then the results must be discarded. This check is simplest for mass normalised vectors since in this case both $\phi_i{}^t M\phi_i$ and $\phi_j{}^t M\phi_j$ are unity and the absolute value of $\phi_i{}^t M\phi_j$ is meaningful. A similar orthogonality check can be made on the stiffness by comparing $\phi_i{}^t K\phi_j$ with the smaller of $\phi_i{}^t K\phi_i$ and $\phi_j{}^t K\phi_j$ provided that neither $\phi_i$ or $\phi_j$ correspond to zero eigenvalue (rigid body) modes.

This check can be expensive to carry out and is rarely done in practice. Instead the convergence of each eigenvalue is traced as the solution progresses and some systems print out some form of convergence measure for each mode. This gives an indication as to how reliable the corresponding eigenvalue and vector is likely to be. The exact meaning of such a measure depends upon the system, the eigenvalue extraction scheme used and how the accuracy is checked.

## 8.8 Sturm Sequence Checks

The eigenvalue extraction schemes used in most structural analysis programs are designed to find the first few lowest modes of vibration. There is always a danger with schemes designed to do this that some of the modes in the range have been missed. The Sturm sequence check provides a technique for estimating if any of the modes have in fact been missed. If the i'th resonant frequency is $\omega_i$ then a value $g = (1+f)\omega_i{}^2$ is taken, (where f is typically 0.01), and the equations $(K - gM)$ are set up. These are factorised into the product LU using Gauss elimination. L is a lower triangular matrix and U is upper triangular with unit values down the leading diagonal. The product of the terms down the leading diagonal of L gives the value of the determinant $(K - gM)$. Each time one of the leading diagonal terms in L is negative then the determinant of a principal minor changes sign. It can be shown that the number of sign changes of the principal minors is equal to the number of eigenvalues below g. Numerically this is a very stable process since it only depends upon the the signs of the numbers and not their actual values.

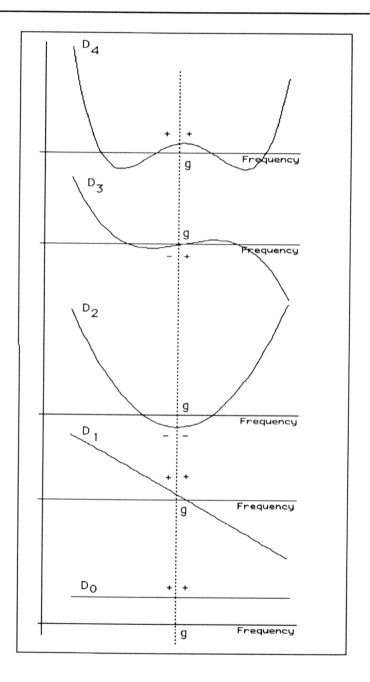

Fig 8.3 - Sturm Sequence Count

The Sturm sequence process is relatively expensive to compute and is normally only used for checking purposes. It can also be used before the eigenvalue extraction is run to tell the user how many modes to ask for within a frequency range. This can be useful if there is a data error, say the density has been incorrectly specified, in which case the Sturm sequence check will indicate that there are no modes or that there is a very large number of modes in the range of interest. This can also indicate modelling problems with very detailed models, typically the existence of many low frequency panel modes. If the overall response is required the panels can be omitted. The Sturm sequence check is the only method available to give an indication of the number of modes within a frequency range. Almost all other eigenvalue extraction techniques calculate from the lowest up or the highest down.

This is illustrated graphically in figure 8.3, for a system with four degrees of freedom. The variations of the determinant $D$ of each principal minor functions is plotted against g. The actual eigenvalues are the zeros of the top curve for $D_4=(K-gM)_4$. In this example there are four eigenvalues. Taking the dotted vertical line for the chosen value of g and counting the number of sign changes with the value of the determinant of each principal minor, $D_i=(K-gM)_i$, then the sign count gives two eigenvalues below the guess, g, which is correct. The stability of the method can be illustrated by considering that a numerical rounding error causes the computed value of the determinant of $D_3 = (K-gM)_3$ to have the wrong sign. This is illustrated by the + sign to the right of the dotted line in figure 8.3 for the $D_3$ curve. Even with this error there is still only a total of two sign changes and the result is still correct.

It is an extremely reliable method for finding the number of eigenvalues below g. If this is equal to the number found from the eigenvalue extraction then there are none missing but if it is greater then the difference gives the number missed. Eigenvalues can be missed for various reasons depending upon the extraction scheme used. Typically for a two dimensional straight beam analysis some modes are axial motions and some are transverse bending and there is no coupling between them. It is quite possible for an extraction scheme to miss all or some of one set of modes, say the axial ones, whilst calculating all of the the bending set. To find the missing modes usually requires a re-analysis with either different starting conditions, requesting more modes or specifying a different convergence tolerance. If uncoupled sets of modes occur, either because motions in some planes are independent of motions in others or because the structure has lines of symmetry it is better to take advantage of this by solving for each set separately by the use of appropriate boundary conditions. There are some extraction schemes that are prone to missing modes if multiple eigenvalues occur. For example, the Lanczos method with exact arithmetic will only find one of a set of multiple modes. In practice rounding error means that they are recovered back into the system but it can take a significant number of extra Lanczos vectors before this occurs. These can usually only be found by requesting that more modes are calculated.

## 8.9 Damped Eigenvalues and Eigenvectors

Relatively few systems allow the user to find the eigenvalues and vectors of arbitrarily damped systems. It is more common to assume either modal damping factors for the undamped modes or that the damping distribution is a linear combination of the mass and stiffness in the form $C=(\alpha M+\beta K)$. In either case the eigenvectors of the damped system are identical to the undamped vectors and these can be used for response calculations. The eigenvalues of the damped system are not the same as the undamped ones but they can be found from the undamped ones as

$$\omega_{jd} = \omega_{ju}(-\xi_j +- i(1- \xi_j^2)^{1/2})$$

where $\omega_{ju}= \lambda_j^{1/2}$ is the undamped resonant frequency of the j'th mode and $\xi_j$ is the damping factor for the j'th mode. If proportional damping is used then

$$\xi_j = \frac{( \alpha/\omega_{ju} + \beta\omega_{ju})}{2}$$

It will be seen from this that for damping factors less than one, which is usually the case for structural vibrations, the damped resonant frequencies are complex and occur as complex conjugate pairs. For systems that do calculate the eigenvalues and vectors of arbitrarily damped systems then, for light damping, the resulting eigenvalues are complex. The real part of the eigenvalue is proportional to the modal damping factor and is always negative for positive damping. The imaginary part is the damped natural frequency. For viscous damping the eigenvalues are complex conjugate pairs. The eigenvectors (mode

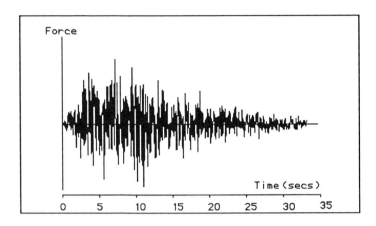

Fig 8.4 - Seismic Time History

shapes) will also occur as complex conjugate vectors. They can be normalised in the same way as the undamped vectors. The complex nature of the vectors means physically that the the displacements within a mode do not all peak at the same time and the ratio of the real to imaginary part for a displacement gives the phase angle at which that degree of freedom has its maximum value.

For material (or hysteretic) damping the eigenvalues and vectors are again complex but they are no longer complex conjugate pairs. This form of material damping is only valid in the frequency domain and should not be used in the time domain where it can lead to unstable solutions. Very few, if any, systems allow arbitrary material damping

## 8.10  Minimising the Output for Time Domain Response

When minimising the output for a time history response, two different aspects have to be considered. The response will vary spatially over the structure and it will also vary with time. It follows that, for peak responses, the user requires results at positions of maximum response on the structure at the times where the maximum time response occurs. If a modal solution is being used then this affords the analyst with a very convenient set of results for minimising the data output. A modal solution implies that only a small subset of the lowest modes of the structure are being used for the response calculation so that the data implied by the modal solution is less than that of the complete system. Further the modal solution neatly separates the response into the spatial and the time variations. The spatial variation of the response is defined by the mode shapes.

Before any time response calculation is conducted the stress distribution for each mode can be found by treating the mode shape as a displacement vector. Since this can be multiplied by an arbitrary scaling factor the absolute magnitude of the stresses have no meaning but, within a mode, the pattern of the stress distribution is correct. This allows the user to identify the nodes in the structure that will have the maximum stress response for that mode. The nodes with the largest values in the mode shape itself will indicate where the maximum displacement (and velocity and accelerations) are likely to occur. This is repeated for each mode that is used in the analysis allowing the user to build up a table of nodes defining the possible locations of the maximum stress and the maximum displacement. Note that the maximum stress will rarely if ever occur at the same point as the maximum displacements. Since the modes can combine in a subtractive sense as well as being additive it can not be guaranteed that the peak values occur at the peak nodal positions. However, it does give a small subset of nodes that are likely to be highly stressed and these can be investigated first. The times at which these give peak values can then be used as indicators as to which times to recover and investigate the stresses at all of the nodes.

Similarly the time variation is contained in the modal responses and there are only as many of these as modes used in the analysis. The modal responses can be plotted and inspected for the times when they have absolute maximum values and these times used to define when the response of the complete system is to be found. The maximum values of the modal response can be used with confidence since they will not contain any rigid body components to give a false origin for the elastic response. The combination of positions of the peak spatial values and the peak response times means that only a very limited amount of data need be recovered on a restart for the stress or displacement response.

The use of the response in each mode as a means of determining the time interval over which to recover the response is shown in figures 8.4 and 8.5. For this analysis a relatively complicated structure was excited by the seismic wave shown in figure 8.4. It will be seen

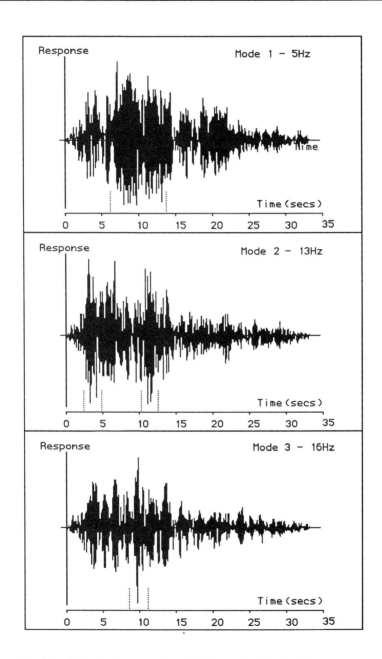

Fig 8.5 - Seismic Response Time Histories For Modes 1-3

that this is a complicated time history that starts to rise significantly after about 1.5 seconds and is relatively strong up to about 12 seconds with a significant tail in the response up to at least 20 seconds. This is a long time to calculate all of the displacements and stresses for the 3000 degree of freedom model actually used in this example. The first 30 modes of vibration were found for the model and the 30 modal responses calculated and plotted for the time history. The modal response of the first three modes are shown in figure 8.5, where a damping of 3% critical was assumed in all of the modes. The regions of strong response are shown by the dotted lines on the figure. The first mode has a relatively high response from about 6 to 14 seconds. The second mode has two periods of high response, the first from 3 to 5 seconds and the second from 10 to 12 seconds. These periods correspond to the times when the 'constant' strong motion starts and when it finishes. The second mode has a resonant frequency of 13 Hz compared to 5Hz for the first so that the response dies away over a shorter time. The third mode has its highest response in the 8 to 11 second band. All of the other modes had characteristics similar to modes two and three. Since the total response is only a linear combination of the various modal responses it can be safely said that the peak structural response will occur somewhere in the time interval 3 to 14 seconds and only this section of the thirty second input motion time need be considered. The nodal responses need only be recovered over this reduced time interval and, more importantly from the point of view of computational efficiency, the stresses only have to be calculated in this time interval. The figures given here are quite typical and illustrate how the need to calculate the full response can be minimised.

It is not so easy to minimise the data output when the solution involves some form of time integration. If the program keeps a record of the maximum values of the response at each node and the time that these occur then this can be inspected to determine at what positions and what times the response must be calculated in detail to obtain information on how it is responding. This maximum response file must contain records for all of the information that is required by the user, typically the maximum values at all of the nodes of the displacements, velocities, accelerations and stresses, although an equivalent stress or strain energy density value at the nodes is sufficient to identify maximum values rather than all of the stress components. If a record of maximum responses is not provided then it requires experience on the part of the analyst to decide what values to track as the solution proceeds. These responses are investigated in detail to find the times of maximum response and the solution for the complete structure is displayed for times around these maxima. The analyst must check to confirm that the values that were tracked do represent the peak values. If they do not then the investigation should be repeated using more realistic values to track the peaks.

## 8.11  Minimising the Output for Frequency Domain Response

As with the solution in the time domain a modal solution allows the user the best way of minimising the output data. The mode shape and the modal stress distribution can again be used to define the points on the structure where the maximum response occurs. If the structure is lightly damped, and most structures are, then the peak response will occur around each resonance. If the resonant frequency is $\omega_r$ and the damping factor is $\xi$ then the peak response will occur over the frequency range $\omega_r-\omega_d$ to $\omega_r+\omega_d$ where $\omega_d=\omega_r/\xi$. The user should then concentrate the response recovery in this range for each resonance. Some programs do this automatically. The response between resonances tends to be reasonably flat and can be calculated at a relatively small number of points without any loss of information.

It is much more difficult to minimise the output if a dynamic stiffness solution is carried out with no knowledge of the resonant frequencies. For lightly damped systems it is very easy to miss a resonant response. To avoid this requires either that the response is found at a very large number of frequency points or, as the dynamic stiffness solution progresses the equivalent of a Sturm sequence check is carried out to identify the regions where resonances occur.

## 8.12  Minimising the Output for a Stationary Random Response

A stationary random response is carried out in the frequency domain and all of the comments of the previous section are relevant here. It is even more important to have a knowledge of the resonant frequencies since the spectral density involves the square of the response and this squaring makes the resonant peaks appear even sharper. Also the mean square of the response is the area under the spectral density curve. For lightly damped systems the majority of this area is under a narrow band around each resonant peak. It is essential to have the shape of the spectral density curve well defined around each resonance if the mean square response of a lightly damped system is required.

## 8.13 The Role of Graphics in the Presentation of Dynamic Results

The use of graphics for presenting results for a static analysis is now a very much accepted practice. It allows the analyst to comprehend the response much more easily than by tables of numbers, allowing him to quickly make judgments regarding the validity of the solution. Graphics are even more important when investigating a dynamic response. All of the graphics features that are used for statics can be used for dynamics. These include:

a.   Displaced shape plots. These can either be a plot of a mode shape or an instantaneous snapshot of the displacement at any time or frequency. Deformed plots of the instantaneous velocities and accelerations can also be produced although these are more difficult to understand since they do not represent a physical shape. If the response is in the frequency domain then it must be given at some angle within the response cycle. This is especially true for systems with non-proportional damping since all points do not peak at the same point in the cycle in this case. Note that displaced shape plots of response spectra calculations have no meaning since these displacements are always positive and do not represent any physical shape.

b.   Contour plots. These can be stress contours for a snapshot of the stress state at any instant of time or frequency or they can be contours of absolute displacements velocities or accelerations to show where the maximum response occurs. Again the output from response spectrum calculations are only maximum stress values and are all positive. They should not be used for any other processing such as finding principal stresses. This should be done before the response spectrum combination of the modal values is computed if they are required

c.   Graph plots. These can be plots of stress or displacement along a line through the structure, exactly as for a static analysis, or plots of response with time or frequency. For the frequency response the graphics system should also allow either the phase angle or the in phase and out of phase components to be plotted. If a random response has been found then facilities should be available for plotting spectral densities for both auto and cross spectra.

All of the other plotting facilities such as sectioning, windowing and selective element plots are just as useful for dynamics as they are for statics.

In addition animation facilities adds a new, very useful, presentation facility for dynamic analysis. Animated mode shapes are usually formed by drawing and saving a series of frames for the shape at various points as the structure oscillates through one cycle. These are then displayed in rapid succession to give an animated mode plot. This gives a much more informative presentation than a single picture, often allowing displacements to be clearly seen where such movement was not obvious from single pictures. Animated plots in this form can also be used to display response in the frequency domain. Ten frames are sufficient for animated modes or frequency response. Animated plots are equally useful for displaying response in the time domain allowing such phenomena as wave propagation to be clearly seen. However, in practice it is currently not possible, on most computers, to save sufficient frames in the computer memory to allow the response over a significant number of steps to be displayed. This is becoming less of a limitation as the amount of computing power available to each user increases. Animation is generally only possible on single user computers or workstations or with sophisticated graphics terminals linked to a main frame. If the computer response is slow for any reason then the animated plot can be very jerky and difficult to interpret. Facilities are now becoming available for drawing frames onto video tapes to allow animation to be displayed externally to the computer. This can display a long duration response but the graphical resolution is quite low.

Figure 8.6 shows some typical ways of plotting mode shape data for an elliptical plate vibrating normal to its surface. The plot in the top left hand window shows the outline of the plate and the nodal lines (lines of zero displacement) are superimposed upon this. In the top right hand window the outline mode shape and the nodal lines are plotted together to give another form of visualisation. The lower two windows show the more conventional distorted mesh plot for the mode, one with just the distorted mesh and the second the distorted mesh superimposed upon a dashed line plot of the undistorted mesh. It is

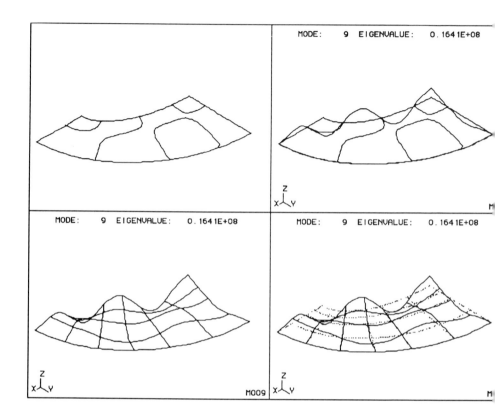

<u>Fig 8.6 - Typical Results Plots</u>

convenient to be able to plot the modes in these various forms since they are all useful. They could all be superimposed together but then the plot would contain too much information and be difficult to interpret. The plot in the bottom right hand window is already becoming rather cluttered.

## 8.14 The Importance of Pilot Studies in Results Presentation

It is very difficult, even with considerable experience, to predict what the response of a structure to some form of dynamic forcing is going to be. This makes it difficult to decide what components of the input are most significant and to decide what aspects of the response should be investigated. A reliable result is usually obtained in the shortest time by approaching the full analysis via one or more simplified pilot studies. Apart, possibly, from the case of a very short duration impulse or impact problem, the analyst should always make some estimate for the mode shapes and frequencies even if a modal solution is not being used. A knowledge of the frequencies is useful to decide:

a.  Whether a time varying force is of a short or long duration. If the lowest mode has a period T then an input is of a short duration if it changes rapidly over a time less than 0.1T and is of a long duration if it does not change significantly over the time T.

b.  What time steps to display (as opposed to calculating) the response at. Again, if the lowest mode has a period of T then the response should be found at times of at least 0.5T intervals. If the force input is changing over a shorter time interval than this, then the response should be displayed at times corresponding to how rapidly the force is changing.

c.  To decide where to concentrate the response points in a frequency domain or stationary random response.

A knowledge of the mode shapes allows the user to choose where to recover the response on the structure as described above. Knowing the resonant frequencies and mode shapes is also very useful for interpreting the results as described below. To be useful in this context the frequencies and mode shapes do not have to be very accurate since they are being used as guides. Sufficiently accurate estimates can be obtained from either a heavily condensed model of the actual structure under analysis or from a very simplified model of the structure.

The construction of an initial very simplified model is always a good thing to do when carrying out a dynamic analysis as it allows the fundamental dynamic parameters of the system to be found quickly and these can then be very useful in deciding what degree of modelling is required for the actual analysis. It also gives the analyst a feel for the dynamic response of the structure so that errors are detected at an early stage.

## 8.15  Methods  of  Stress  Recovery

If a direct integration or dynamic stiffness solution procedure has been adopted then the full displacement vector is available at any time or at any frequency, allowing the stress to be found from this in exactly the same way that is done for statics. If a modal solution has been used then there are two ways that the stress can be recovered.

The first method, which is computationally the cheapest, again just computes the stresses directly from the displacements. However, this displacement vector will now only be a linear combination of the mode shapes that have been used and since these are only the first few lowest modes some information must have been lost in the response calculation. The lowest modes tend to be those displaced shapes that minimise the strain energy and maximise the kinetic energy. A stress concentration does exactly the opposite in that the displaced shape in this case will tend to maximise the strain energy whilst minimising the kinetic energy. In other words, the lowest modes of vibration tend to be those displaced shapes that filter out stress concentration effects. If the aim of the analysis is to find the magnitude of the stresses then use of the lower modes will give considerable errors when calculating stress concentrations. Where the structure does not have any significant stress concentrations then stresses found directly from the displacements will be substantially correct provided that there is a sufficient number of modes used to make the velocity response correct.

To overcome this there is a second, more accurate, method of recovering the stresses. In this the acceleration vector is computed from the modal response. These are multiplied by the mass matrix to give the instantaneous inertia forces which are then applied as static loads to the complete structure. The full set of displacements found by solving the equation

$$\mathbf{K} \mathbf{r} = \mathbf{R} - \mathbf{M} \phi \, \ddot{\mathbf{q}}$$

where $\mathbf{K}$ is the stiffness matrix, $\mathbf{r}$ the required displacements, $\mathbf{M}$ the mass matrix, $\phi$ the set of eigenvectors that have been used and $\ddot{\mathbf{q}}$ the modal accelerations. $\mathbf{R}$ is the applied force at the instant of time that is being considered. The equations are solved for the displacements $\mathbf{r}$, exactly as in a static analysis. Since these are found using the complete stiffness matrix they will contain the effect of any stress concentrations. This increased accuracy is obtained at the expense of a considerable increase in cost since a set of equations must now be solved at each time point that the stress is recovered.

In many cases the first method of stress recovery will be quite adequate but not if stress concentrations are present. If an analyst is in doubt as to which method to use a simple test can be conducted. A static (zero frequency) problem can be solved as a dynamic problem using the set of modes that are to be used for the full analysis. The stresses from this can be compared with a static solution stress distribution for the same load. If the peak stresses are substantially the same then the first method can be used for the dynamic stress recovery. If there is an appreciable difference between the two sets of results then the second method must be used for the recovery of the dynamic stresses.

# CHAPTER 9 - RANDOM VIBRATIONS AND SEISMIC ANALYSIS

## 9.1 Introduction

There are some occasions when the dynamic loading on a structure cannot be defined precisely. Typically, an aircraft flying through turbulent air will experience dynamic loads but, because of the nature of turbulence, these loads will be different if a second identical aircraft flies through the same the same volume of air at some other time. Although the time histories of the two loadings are not identical they do have similar characteristics and an estimate of the dynamic response of both aircraft can be computed. In order to do this the load has to be defined somehow even though it is random. Any random event arising from some physical consequence will obey the physical laws associated with the cause of the event, so that the average characteristics of the event are retained. A random vibration analysis uses these average quantities to define both the forcing function and the response. The actual solution methods used for solving random vibration problems are basically the same as for a deterministic analysis but they have to be modified to work in terms of averages rather than precise quantities. This leads to a new set of terms for random vibration analysis that makes the subject rather impenetrable at first. However, once the basic terms and ideas are understood then most of the considerations of a conventional deterministic dynamic analysis are applicable to random vibrations.

## 9.2 Mean Quantities

In order to define random quantities a conceptual model of the random event must be defined. This is achieved by considering that there are an infinite number of identical structures all being excited simultaneously by the random event. Since the event is random each one of these infinity of structures will experience a different forcing function from any other. The concept of an infinite number of events occurring simultaneously allows the values of each one of these events to be considered at the same time t. The average, or mean, value of the event at time t is then the average of all of these simultaneous events at that time. For most structural vibrations the force alternates evenly about zero so that the mean value of both the force and response are zero. If the force does have a non-zero mean then, in order to guarantee that some of the random relationships are always valid, it is usually subtracted from the random signal to give a zero mean event. One of the most useful quantities that can be defined simply is the mean square value of the signal at time t. This is obtained by taking the value of any one event at time t, squaring it and the averaging this squared quantity across all of the infinite number of events. The mean square value will only be zero if the values of all of the events are simultaneously zero. In general it is some positive number. Note care must be taken with the terminology used. For a random signal its mean square value is not the same as the mean squared (that is the square of the mean). For a zero mean process the square of the mean is always zero but the mean square is always a positive, usually non-zero, number. The mean square is important since it is easily measured and it also characterises other quantities used in random vibration theory. There is no reason why this idea cannot be extended to higher order means so that, typically, a mean cube quantity can be defined as the average of the cube of the values of all of the events at time t.

## 9.3 Stationary and Ergodic Processes

In many cases if the mean and mean square and any other statistical quantity is computed at various times they are found to be constant. If this is the case the process is said to be stationary. A stationary process is one where its average characteristics do not change with time. A further definition is also required in that, conceptually, it is possible to imagine the infinite number of simultaneous events to have stationary characteristics even if the time history of any two events do not look the same. If all of the event time histories have the same general look then they are said to be ergodic, that is any one sample is completely representative of all of the other samples of the event. If a stationary ergodic process can be assumed (generally referred to as just a stationary process) then the random response calculations are simplified considerably. Most random vibration analysis assumes that the excitation signal is stationary. In this case, provided that the structural behaviour is linear, then the response is also stationary. Techniques for solving stationary random vibration problems are well developed. However, there are some practical situations where the random forcing function is non-stationary. The most common example of this is a seismic or earthquake event. Each earthquake in geologically similar regions have the same general characteristics but they are not stationary. The signal starts at a low level, rises to a high value, possibly holds this high value for some time and then falls back to the low level. General random vibration analysis theory is not well developed for such excitations and special approximate solution techniques have been developed.

## 9.4 Practical Considerations

The idealised random system described above cannot be achieved in practice. Instead it is approximated by taking either a series of samples of the random event (the random forcing function) or by taking a very long recording for one sample and splitting this up into a series of events. Each one of these samples is then used as one of the 'infinite number' of events in the idealised model. Provided that there are a sufficient number of samples and that each sample occurs for a sufficiently long time then this approximates to the idealised model. For a more detailed discussion of this and how to assess if a sufficient number of samples have been used refer to the book by Bendat and Piersol. It is assumed in the rest of this chapter that the data is known sufficiently well to define its random characteristics exactly. If the random characteristics are found from the analysis of one single long sample it is an implied assumption that the process is ergodic. If the signal is non-stationary it is not likely that a sufficient number of samples will be available to characterise it in a random fashion since one long sample cannot be captured. In this case a lower confidence level in the precise nature of the forcing function must be accepted.

## 9.5 Probability Distributions and Probability Density Functions

The random characteristics of a forcing function or of a response implies that it is impossible to say exactly what the amplitude of either will be at any time. Instead, the best that can be done is to give an estimate of what the probable value of the quantity of interest is going to be together with what the chances are of it being any other value. This is done by finding the probability distribution or the probability density function of the signal.

These two quantities are closely related with the probability density function being the derivative of the probability distribution curve. Considering the infinite number of random events all occurring simultaneously then at any time, t, these can be investigated to see how many samples have a value greater than a specified value v. The number that are less than or equal to the specified value divided by the total number of samples is called the probability distribution for v. This can then be plotted for all values of v to give the probability distribution curve. The number of samples less than v can never be less than zero and, equally, it can never be greater than the total number of samples available. This means that the probability distribution curve changes monotonically from zero to one. If it changes smoothly the event is continuous, which is usually the case for random vibrations. By definition for a stationary process the probability distribution curve is independent of the time at which it was sampled.

The derivative of the probability distribution curve is the probability density function and this is the form that is generally used. The chance that any value of the event lies between v and v+dv is given by the value of the probability density function at v multiplied by dv. For any event the probability density function should be measured. In practice this is rarely if ever done. Instead the process is assumed to have a normal or Gaussian distribution. It is often a very good assumption since it can be shown that if a random process is generated by the superposition of a large number of random sources, none of which are dominant, then the resultant random process will be approximately normal. This means that most naturally occurring forcing functions for a dynamic analysis are Gaussian. Further, if a linear system is excited by a forcing function that has a Gaussian distribution then the response will also have a Gaussian distribution. In addition, the Gaussian distribution has the unusual property of being defined by the simple parameters of the mean and the mean square of the process. Most other probability density functions require a much more complicated description. If a process is Gaussian then only the mean and mean square have to be found to be able to say what the chances are of any specified value occurring. Mathematically the Gaussian probability density function is defined as

$$p(v) = \frac{e^{\{\frac{-(v-m)^2}{2\sigma^2}\}}}{(2\pi)^{1/2}\sigma}$$

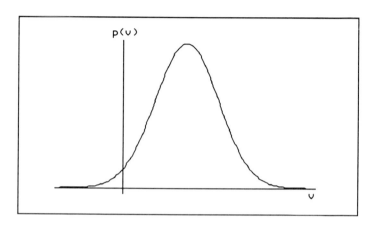

Fig 9.1 - Non Zero Mean Gaussian Probability Density Function

where p(v)dv is the chance that the signal lies between v and v+dv, m is the mean of the signal. $\sigma$ is called the standard deviation and $\sigma^2$ the difference between the mean square

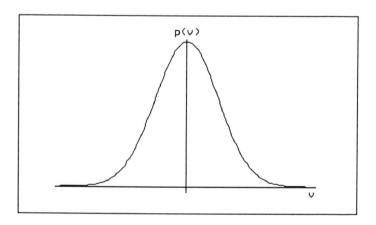

Fig 9.2 - Zero Mean Gaussian Probability Density Function

and the square of the mean. This is plotted in figure 9.1. For a zero mean process the Gaussian distribution is

$$p(v) = \frac{e^{-0.5(v/\sigma)^2}}{(2\pi)^{1/2}\sigma}$$

and $\sigma$ is the root mean square of the signal. The zero mean normal distribution is shown in figure 9.2.

There are many other probability density functions but for random vibrations the Gaussian distribution is the most useful. In some cases the Rayleigh distribution is used. This is similar to the Gaussian distribution but is valid where all of the samples have to be positive. This is the case if the mean square stress is the function being considered or where, say, the probable length of a member is being defined since this can not be negative. There are also non-continuous distributions, such as the Poisson distribution, but these have more use in quantum physics where jumps occur in the system rather than it being a smooth function. These are less useful for random structural vibration analysis but have been used to model noise in electronic circuits.

## 9.6 More than One Variable, Correlation and Spectral Density

All of the definitions given so far only involve a single variable v. In practice the interaction between two or more variables is often required. If values of a displacement at two different times are known then the velocity can be found. In random terms if the probable value of a displacement is known at two times then the probable velocity can be found. Similarly, if the probable values of the displacements at two points in space are known at the same time then the probable strain and stress can be found. The same approach is adopted for two variables as for one. The mean square value of a variable is the average of the square of the ensemble values. For two variables this can be generalised by averaging the product of the variable at time t with the same variable at time t+τ. This gives the autocorrelation of the variable. If the variable is a displacement then, since it involves values of the same variable at two different times, it contains information regarding the velocity. Similarly if the correlation involves displacements at two different points then it contains information regarding the strains. For a stationary process the average quantities are independent of the time t. If the process is stationary then the correlation is only a function of the time difference, $\tau$, and not the absolute time t. A special case occurs for $\tau=0$ since the autocorrelation then becomes the mean square value. There is no reason why the correlation should be restricted to the product of the same variable. The displacement at time t can be multiplied with the force at time $t+\tau$ to give the cross-correlation between the force and the displacement. The cross-correlation between the displacements at two different points at two different times can also be found. In matrix terms say there are a set of displacements over a structure at time t with a value $\mathbf{r}(t)$ and at the time $t+\tau$ they have the value $\mathbf{r}(t+\tau)$ then the correlation matrix is the mean of

$$\mathbf{R}(\tau) = \mathbf{r}(t)\mathbf{r}^t(t+\tau) = \begin{bmatrix} r_1(t)r_1(t+\tau) & r_1(t)r_2(t+\tau) & r_1(t)r_3(t+\tau) & \dots\dots & r_1(t)r_n(t+\tau) \\ r_2(t)r_1(t+\tau) & r_2(t)r_2(t+\tau) & r_2(t)r_3(t+\tau) & \dots\dots & r_2(t)r_n(t+\tau) \\ \cdot & \cdot & \cdot & \dots\dots & \cdot \\ \cdot & \cdot & \cdot & \dots\dots & \\ r_n(t)r_1(t+\tau) & r_n(t)r_2(t+\tau) & r_n(t)r_3(t+\tau) & \dots\dots & r_n(t)r_n(t+\tau) \end{bmatrix}$$

which is a square (nxn) matrix if the structure has n degrees of freedom. The leading diagonal of the matrix gives the autocorrelation of the variables and the off-diagonal terms give the cross correlations. From the definitions of the correlation functions and the mean square values the terms down the leading diagonal of $\mathbf{R}(\tau)$ when $\tau=0$ are the mean square values of the variables.

The correlation terms are useful for developing the equations for the mathematical theory of random vibrations but they are not very useful for practical calculations. The problem arises when the response theory is developed where it is found that the convolution integral relating the response to the loading has to be integrated between times minus infinity and plus infinity. The calculations are simplified considerably if the equations are transformed to the frequency domain. The simplification arises since the process is stationary and only the stationary response has to be computed. This corresponds exactly to steady state solutions for a deterministic analysis and these are also found most easily in the frequency domain. The transformation to the frequency domain is achieved by means of the Fourier transformation and applying the Fourier transform to the correlation matrix gives the spectral density matrix $\mathbf{S}(\omega)$.

$$S(\omega) = \frac{1}{2\pi} \int_{-\infty}^{\infty} R(\tau)\, e^{-i\omega\tau} d\tau$$

The inverse transformation gives

$$R(\tau) = \int_{-\infty}^{\infty} S(\omega)\, e^{i\omega\tau} d\omega$$

The factor $1/2\pi$ has to be include in these pair of equations but how and where it is included is rather arbitrary leading to slightly different definitions of the transformations, but when the pair are considered together the definitions are always consistent. The spectral density is a function of frequency, $\omega$, and gives the frequency content of the random signal. The diagonal terms of the spectral density matrix gives the power spectral density or the auto spectral density of each variable. These terms are always real positive numbers. The off-diagonal terms are called the cross spectral densities. They are generally complex numbers with the real part being the in phase component and the imaginary part being the out of phase component between the two signals involved in the cross spectral density. The real part of the spectral density matrix is symmetric and the complex part is skew symmetric, so that if

$$S_{ij}(\omega) = a + ib$$

then

$$S_{ji}(\omega) = a - ib \quad \text{and} \quad S_{ii}(\omega) \text{ is wholly real}$$

A matrix with this structure of the real part being symmetric and the imaginary part being skew symmetric is said to be an Hermitian matrix.

The mean square response can be found from the correlation function at $\tau=0$

$$\text{mean square} = R_{ii}(0) = \int_{-\infty}^{\infty} S_{ii}(\omega)\, e^{i\omega 0} d\omega = \int_{-\infty}^{\infty} S_{ii}(\omega)\, d\omega$$

so that the mean square response can be found by calculating the area under the spectral density curve.

## 9.7 Stationary Response

The deterministic steady state solution in the frequency domain can be written as (see sections 2.5 and 2.12 )

$$g(\omega) = H(\omega) \, G(\omega)$$

where $H(\omega)$ is called the dynamic flexibility matrix. It is a function of frequency and, if damping is included in the system, it is a complex matrix. In random terms, if the forcing function has a known spectral density matrix $S_{RR}(\omega)$, then the spectral density matrix of the response is

$$S_{rr}(\omega) = \bar{H}(\omega) \, S_{RR}(\omega) \, H^t(\omega)$$

where $\bar{H}(\omega)$ is the complex conjugate of the dynamic flexibility matrix. This form of matrix multiplication preserves the Hermitian characteristics of the spectral density so that the spectral density of the response, $S_{rr}(\omega)$, is also Hermitian in form. This calculation is repeated for each frequency of interest. It forms the basis of most random response calculations. It can be carried further since, by using standard finite element theory, the stresses at any point can be expressed in terms of the displacements as

$$\sigma = \alpha r$$

which gives the spectral density of the stresses at the point as

$$S_{\sigma\sigma}(\omega) = \alpha \, S_{rr}(\omega) \, \alpha^t$$

and so on for any other derived quantity.

When defining the forcing function for a deterministic response it is only necessary to define the force at each point on the structure. For stationary random excitation the

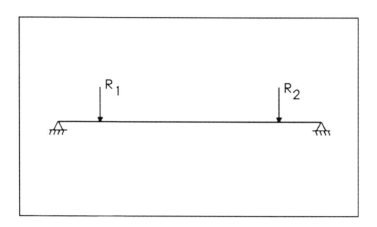

Fig 9.3 - Beam with Two Random Forces

relationship between the forces are also required. For example, consider the simple beam model shown in figure 9.3. This has two excitation forces, $R_1$ and $R_2$ and the spectral density matrix will be a (2x2) matrix.

$$S_{RR} = \begin{bmatrix} S_{11} & S_{12} \\ S_{21} & S_{22} \end{bmatrix}$$

In this the power spectrum term $S_{11}$ is defined entirely by the random characteristics of the force $R_1$. Similarly, the power spectrum term $S_{22}$ is defined entirely by the random characteristics of the force $R_2$. The difference from a conventional deterministic response lies in the fact that the cross-spectrum terms, $S_{12}$ and $S_{21}$, are defined by the relative dynamic characteristics of the two forces. If $R_1$ and $R_2$ are statistically independent then the cross terms are zero, $S_{12} = S_{21} = 0$. At the other extreme, the two forces can have identical time histories in which case $S_{11} = S_{22} = S_{12} = S_{21} \neq 0$. If $R_1$ and $R_2$ have the same time history but have opposite signs (that is a 180 degree phase shift) then $S_{11} = S_{22} = -S_{12} = -S_{21} \neq 0$. Similarly if they have a ninety degree phase shift then $S_{11} = S_{22} = iS_{12} = -iS_{21} \neq 0$. where i denotes the square root of minus 1. If the two forces are partially related then all that can be said is that $S_{12}$ is the complex conjugate of $S_{21}$. The response of the system will be very different under these different conditions. Typically the case where the two forces are exactly the same ($S_{11} = S_{22} = S_{12} = S_{21}$) will excite the symmetric modes of the beam in figure 9.3 but the case where they have opposite signs ($S_{11} = S_{22} = -S_{12} = -S_{21}$) will excite only the anti-symmetric modes.

If all of the forces come from different sources then it is unlikely that they will be correlated and the spectral density matrix can be assumed to be diagonal. This is rarely the case. More common is the situation where all of the forces on the structure arise from one single cause. In this case the forces will be highly correlated and the cross-spectral terms will not be zero. The magnitude of the correlation depends upon the nature of the forcing function and how it is applied to the structure. If the basic excitation is some distance from the structure and it travels along the same path before it reaches the points on the structure that are excited then it can usually be considered to be fully correlated. If, however, it is applied close to the structure or it travels along various different paths before it reaches the structure then it is correlated to some extent but not completely. In such cases separate estimates have to be made for the cross-spectral terms, either by separate calculation or based upon experience or testing. If the source of the random excitation occurs at one point on the structure but it is felt at many other points (say a body with fluid flowing over it where the flow changes from laminar to turbulent at some point on the body) then the idea of a correlation length can be used. In this case it is assumed that the forces are correlated within some distance from the source, the correlation length, and are totally uncorrelated outside of this.

One special case is where the random excitation is moving with a constant velocity, V, over the structure in the x direction. Typically this can occur with the flow of traffic over a bridge or a seismic wave passing over the base of some plant. In this case the spectral density at any one point is $S_{RR}(\omega)$. Since the excitation is moving with a constant velocity V then some other point a distance x downstream from the first will see exactly the same excitation but at some time x/V later. Hence the spectral density of the force at this point will also be $S_{RR}(\omega)$. What is of interest is are the cross-spectral density terms. These can be found by considering the cross-correlations including the time shift x/V for the second point and then carrying out a Fourier transform on this to give the cross-spectral density. The conclusion is that these terms are:

$$S_{12}(\omega) = e^{i\omega x/V} S_{RR}(\omega) \quad \text{and} \quad S_{21}(\omega) = e^{-i\omega x/V} S_{RR}(\omega).$$

For many excitation points this becomes:

$$S(\omega) = S_{RR}(\omega) \begin{bmatrix} 1 & \exp(-i\omega x_{12}/V) & \cdots & \exp(-i\omega x_{1n}/V) \\ \exp(i\omega x_{21}/V) & 1 & \cdots & \exp(-i\omega x_{2n}/V) \\ \cdot & \cdot & \cdot & \cdot \\ \cdot & \cdot & \cdot & \cdot \\ \exp(i\omega x_{n1}/V) & \exp(i\omega x_{n2}/V) & \cdots & 1 \end{bmatrix}$$

Where $x_{jk}$ is the distance between nodes j and k in the direction that the excitation is travelling. It will be seen that the complete spectral density matrix can be defined in terms of the spectral density at one point in this case.

## 9.8 Stationary Response with Base Movement Excitation

If the random excitation involves a movement of the base then the deterministic problem can be solved by one of the methods of section (3.9.2 ). The fundamental equation of motion with no assumptions other than linearity is:

$$M_{ii}\ddot{r}_i + C_{ii}\dot{r}_i + K_{ii}r_i = - M_{ib}\ddot{r}_b - C_{ib}\dot{r}_b - K_{ib}r_b$$

The excitation terms on the right hand side involve the base displacements, velocities and accelerations. For the deterministic problem, if the time history of the displacements is known then this can be differentiated to give the velocities and differentiated again to give the accelerations. In other words, once the base displacements are known then the right hand side of the equation can be determined in terms of these. The same applies for the random equations. If the spectral density of the base displacements is $S_{bb}(\omega)$ then the complete spectral density matrix for all of the displacements, velocities and accelerations is:

$$\begin{bmatrix} S_{bb}(\omega) & S_{b\dot{b}}(\omega) & S_{b\ddot{b}}(\omega) \\ S_{\dot{b}b}(\omega) & S_{\dot{b}\dot{b}}(\omega) & S_{\dot{b}\ddot{b}}(\omega) \\ S_{\ddot{b}b}(\omega) & S_{\ddot{b}\dot{b}}(\omega) & S_{\ddot{b}\ddot{b}}(\omega) \end{bmatrix} = S_{bb}(\omega) \begin{bmatrix} I & i\omega I & -\omega^2 I \\ -i\omega I & -\omega^2 I & i\omega^3 I \\ -\omega^2 I & -i\omega^3 I & \omega^4 I \end{bmatrix}$$

Where I is the unit matrix. A similar form can be obtained if the acceleration or velocity spectral densities are known.

## 9.9  White Noise

A special form of spectral density is known as white noise. For white noise the spectral density is constant for all frequencies.

$$S(\omega) = S_O$$

where $S_O$ is a constant. This corresponds to an auto-correlation function that is a single spike at $\tau=0$. Such a description is very convenient mathematically but it is impossible to achieve in practice since it implies that the signal has an infinite amount of energy associated with it. In practice this can be approximated experimentally by a signal with a response spectrum that this substantially constant for $\omega=0$ to $\omega=\omega_c$ where $\omega=\omega_c$ is some cut off frequency. Above this the spectral density decreases to zero. The signal then approximates white noise up to the cut off frequency. This is often called pink noise. One way of achieving pink noise is by means of a psuedo- random number sequence.

## 9.10  Narrow Band Random Noise

Another form of spectral density that is found in practice is narrow band noise. In this case the spectral density has a high peak value concentrated over a very narrow frequency range. Such a process is shown in figure 9.4. The time history of a narrow band random process looks very much like a sine wave modulated by random noise. The mean square value of the process can be found by integrating the spectral density curve between the limits $-\omega_c$ to $\omega_c$ where $\omega_c$ is some frequency above that at which the peak response of the curve occurs. Care must be taken when evaluating this by numerical integration since many more integration points are required in the region of the peaks than elsewhere. A narrow band response is generated when a forcing function with a white noise spectrum is applied to a lightly damped (that is almost any structural) system. If the structure has more than one resonance then there can be more than one peak in the response but the magnitude of each subsequent peak will tend to be less than the preceding one so that some cut off frequency,

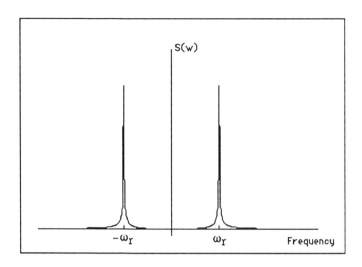

Fig 9.4 - Spectral Density Curve of a Narrow Band Random Process

$\omega_c$, can still be defined. If the structural response is narrow band then techniques are available to determine the fatigue life and probable occurrence of peak failures.

## 9.11  Seismic  Analysis

One form of random excitation found in practice is earthquake or seismic excitation. Unfortunately all of the theory for calculating random vibration response given in the preceding sections is not applicable to this form of excitation because it is non-stationary. The random vibrations start at a low level, rise to a maximum and then fall back to a low level. This means that the signal is non-stationary and hence the above theory is no longer applicable. It is possible to develop theories for the analysis of non-stationary random vibrations but these are not a great deal of use because of the lack of sufficient data to allow the characteristics of the random process to be defined. Instead approximate methods are used to solve for such non-stationary excitations.  One method is to take a series of typical seismic accelographs and to treat these as base accelerations. The structure is analysed for each of these inputs in turn using the accelograph as a deterministic time history in each case. The responses are found and an envelope is then drawn around the maximum responses in order to assess the probable maximum response to any similar seismic excitation. If sufficient suitable seismic traces are available this provides a good estimate of the maximum responses. However, the process is time consuming since each of the time histories have to be solved for. It is found that most earthquakes have insignificant displacements above about 30Hz and this is usually taken as the highest frequency of interest. In order to calculate the response accurately at this frequency the user should aim to model the system such that it can determine the response up to at least 100Hz with a fair degree of accuracy. This means that all resonant frequencies up to this value should be used and the time step used in calculating the response should be no longer than 0.01 seconds. If the seismic event lasts for twenty seconds then at least 2000 time steps have to be computed for each seismic history. If the structural response is non-linear the only method available to find the response is some form of step-by-step time domain calculation.

The time history response calculation is accurate (provided enough histories are used) but it requires many histories to be defined and is time consuming to perform. For these reasons a simpler, but less accurate, technique called the response spectrum method has been developed. It is unfortunate that the name response spectrum is so close to the term spectral density since they are two very different concepts.

## 9.12 Response Spectrum Method

For the response spectrum method it is assumed that the equation of motion can be written in the form:

$$M_{ii}\ddot{s}_i + C_{ii}\dot{s}_i + K_{ii}s_i = -\ddot{\alpha}M_{ii}r_0$$

Where $\ddot{\alpha}$ is the time history of the base accelerations and $r_0$ is the vector of the direction in which the acceleration occurs. This equation is discussed in section (3.9.2) where the assumptions used in its derivation are discussed. Most notably, it is assumed that all of the base movements in a given direction are identical and it is very difficult to relax this assumption when applying the response spectrum method. The eigenvalues and eigenvectors of the equations of motion are computed for resonant frequencies of up to at least 30Hz and these are used to orthogonalise the equations as discussed in section (2.4). A typical modal equation is then:

$$\ddot{q}_i + c_i\dot{q}_i + \omega_i{}^2 q_i = -\ddot{\alpha}\phi_i{}^t M_{ii} r_o = -\ddot{\alpha}p_i$$

Where the eigenvectors have been normalised to make the modal mass values unity hence the modal stiffness is the resonant frequency squared. The term

$$p_i = \phi_i{}^t M_{ii} r_o$$

is called the mass participation factor for the i'th mode. It can be shown that $\sum p_i{}^2$ tends to the total mass of the structure as the number of modes is increased and if the vector $r_o$ corresponds to a rigid body movement. This is often used as a check to ensure that a sufficient number of modes have been used in the analysis. If $\sum p_i{}^2$ corresponds to more than 90% of the total mass then a sufficient number of modes have been used. Note that in some systems this mass participation is printed out for any form of loading, not just the seismic load although, in this form, it is only valid for seismic loads. It is shown in section (3.10.2) that for a general loading it usually underestimates the number of modes required. A more general form applicable to all loads is given in section (3.10.2) and this corresponds exactly to the the mass participation given here for this particular form of seismic loading.

To simplify the calculation procedure a response spectrum curve is generated before the structural analysis is conducted. This is obtained by solving the single degree of freedom equation

$$\ddot{q} + c\dot{q} + \omega^2 q = \ddot{\alpha}$$

where $\omega$ initially is the lowest frequency of interest and c the typical damping value. This is solved in the time domain using the acceleration time history $\ddot{\alpha}$ as the forcing function. The maximum displacement is recorded and this gives one point on the response spectrum curve which is a plot of maximum displacement against frequency. The frequency $\omega$ is then incremented and the solution is repeated to give a second point on the response spectrum curve. The whole process is then repeated over the frequency range of interest to give the response spectrum curve. This whole calculation is then repeated for a series of base excitation histories $\ddot{\alpha}$ to give a series of response spectrum curves all plotted on one graph. An envelope is then drawn around these to give the maximum response that can be expected.

A response spectrum can also be constructed using the maximum velocity as the response that is plotted. A third form uses the maximum acceleration. These are quite closely related in that the acceleration form of the response spectrum is nearly proportional to the displacement form divided by $\omega^2$ and the velocity is nearly proportional to the displacement response spectrum divided by $\omega$. This means that only the velocity spectrum need be computed and the other two can be obtained by rotating the axes by plus and minus forty five degrees and scaling. This gives a tripartite plot typically shown in figure 9.5. Not that both axes for this figure are plotted on a log scale.

Once the response spectrum curve has been generated the structural equations can be set up and the modes and modal participation factors calculated. Knowing the participation factor and the resonant frequency of a mode the modal response can be found without any further calculation merely by interpolating for the value of the response spectrum at the resonant frequency and multiplying this by the participation factor. An assumption then has to be made to find the structural response since the time at which the mode reached its peak value was discarded when the response spectrum was calculated. There is therefore no precise way of combining the modes to allow the total response to be found. There are various appropriate techniques used for doing this. Calling the j'th displacement in the i'th mode $r_{ij}$ then having computed the modal response $q_i$ this is

$$r_{ij} = \phi_{ij}q_i$$

Some of the methods used to combine the modal responses to obtain the total response are

a. The absolute sum

$$r_j = \sum \text{abs}(r_{ij})$$

b. The square root of the sum of the squares (SRSS)

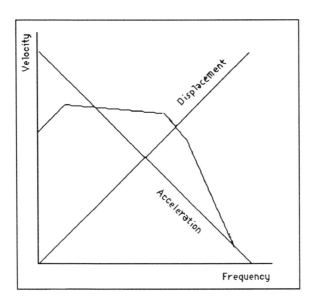

Fig 9.5 - Tripartite Response Spectrum Plot

$$r_j = \sqrt{\Sigma \, r_{ij}^2}$$

c.  The mixed method, where the absolute sum is taken where two modes have frequencies within 10% of each other and the square root of the sum of the squares is taken otherwise.

d.  The complete quadratic combination method (CQC)

$$r_j = \sqrt{\Sigma\Sigma \, r_{ij} \, \rho_{ik} \, r_{kj}}$$

where

$$\rho_{ik} = 8(v_i \, v_j)^{1/2}( \, v_i + \beta v_j) \, \beta^{3/2} / \{(1 - \beta^2)^2 + 4 \, v_i \, v_j \, \beta \, (1 + \beta^2) + 4(v_i^2 + v_j^2) \, \beta^2\}$$

$$v_i = c_i / \{2 \, \omega_i\} \quad \text{and} \quad \beta = \omega_j / \omega_i$$

The absolute sum tends to overestimate the response and can be very conservative. The square root of the sum of the squares is quite accurate where the modes are well separated but tends to under estimate the response when the modes have similar frequencies and they can reach their maximum value almost simultaneously. The mixed method is designed to overcome this objection empirically and the complete quadratic combination to overcome it basing the calculation on what would arise for a stationary random response. There are also a wide variety of other methods but the mixed method or the CQC method are probably as good as any for general use.

# GLOSSARY OF TERMS IN DYNAMIC ANALYSIS

### Accelerance
The same as the inertance.

### Acceleration
The second time derivative of the displacement (the first time derivative of the velocity).

### Algebraic Eigenvalue Problem
The eigenvalue problem when written in the form of stiffness times mode shape minus eigenvalue times mass times mode shape is equal to zero. It is the form that arises naturally from a discrete parameter model in free vibration.

### Characteristic Vector
Same as the eigenvector.

### Characteristic Value
Same as the eigenvalue.

### Complex Eigenvectors
The eigenvectors of a damped system. For proportionally damped systems they are the same as the undamped eigenvectors. For non-proportionally damped systems with damping in all modes less than critical they are complex numbers and occur as complex conjugate pairs.

### Complex Eigenvalues
The eigenvalues of any damped system. If the damping is less than critical they will occur as complex conjugate pairs even for proportionally damped systems. The real

part of the complex eigenvalue is a measure of the damping in the mode and should always be negative. The imaginary part is a measure of the resonant frequency.

## Consistent Displacements and Forces

The displacements and forces act at the same point and in the same direction so that the sum of their products give a work quantity. If consistent displacements and forces are used the the resulting stiffness and mass matrices are symmetric.

## Continuous Mass Models

The system mass is distributed between the degrees of freedom. The mass matrix is not diagonal.

## Continuous Models

The model is defined in terms of partial differential equations rather than in finite degree of freedom matrix form.

## Coefficient(s) of Viscous Damping

The constant(s) of proportionality relating the velocity(ies) to the force(s)

## Constraints

Known values of, or relationships between, the displacements in the coordinate system.

## Coordinate System

The set of displacements used to define the degrees of freedom of the system.

## Critical Damping

The damping value for which the impulse response is just oscillatory.

## Critically Damped System

The dividing line between under damped and over damped systems where the equation of motion has a damping value that is equal to the critical damping.

## Damping
Any mechanism that dissipates energy.

## Damped Eigenvalues
Same as complex eigenvalues.

## Damped Eigenvectors
Same as complex eigenvectors.

## Damping Factor
The ratio of the viscous damping coefficient to the critical damping value.

## Damped Natural Frequency
The frequency at which the damped system vibrates naturally when only an initial disturbance is applied.

## Degrees of Freedom
The number of displacement quantities which must be considered in order to represent the effects of all of the significant inertia forces.

## Deterministic Analysis
The applied loading is a known function of time.

## Discrete Parameter Models
The model is defined in terms of an ordinary differential equation

## Dynamic Flexibility
The factor relating the steady state displacement response of a system to a sinusoidal force input. It is the same as the receptance.

## Dynamic Flexibility Matrix
The matrix relating the complete set of steady state displacement responses to all possible sinusoidal force inputs. It is always symmetric for linear systems. It is the Fourier transform of the impulse response matrix.

## Dynamic Stiffness Matrix

If the structure is vibrating steadily at a frequency w then the dynamic stiffness is $(\mathbf{K}+iw\mathbf{C}-w^2\mathbf{M})$ It is the inverse of the dynamic flexibility matrix.

## Eigenvalues

The roots of the characteristic equation of the system. If a system has n equations of motion then it has n eigenvalues. The square root of the eigenvalues are the resonant frequencies. These are the frequencies that the structure will vibrate at if given some initial disturbance with no other forcing.

## Eigenvectors

The displacement shape that corresponds to the eigenvalues. If the structure is excited at a resonant frequency then the shape that it adopts is the mode shape corresponding to the eigenvalue.

## Ergodic Process

A random process where any one sample record has the same characteristics as any other record.

## Fourier Transform

A method for finding the frequency content of a time varying signal. If the signal is periodic it gives the same result as the Fourier series.

## Fast Fourier Transform

A method for calculating Fourier transforms that is computationally very efficient.

## Frequency Domain

The structures forcing function and the consequent response is defined in terms of their frequency content. The inverse Fourier transform of the frequency domain gives the corresponding quantity in the time domain.

## Fourier Transform Pair

The Fourier transform and its inverse which, together, allow the complete system to be transformed freely in either direction between the time domain and the frequency domain.

## Forced Response

The dynamic motion results from a time varying forcing function.

## Forcing Function

The dynamic forces that are applied to the system.

## Free Vibration

The dynamic motion which results from specified initial conditions. The forcing function is zero.

## Generalised Coordinates

A set of linearly independent displacement coordinates which are consistent with the constraints and are just sufficient to describe any arbitrary configuration of the system. Generalised coordinates are usually patterns of displacements, typically the system eigenvectors.

## Generalised Stiffness

The stiffness associated with a generalised displacement.

## Generalised Mass

The mass associated with a generalised displacement.

## Holonomic Constraints

Constraints that can be defined for any magnitude of displacement.

## Impulse Response Function

The response of the system to an applied impulse.

## Impulse Response Matrix

The matrix of all system responses to all possible impulses. It is always symmetric for linear systems. It is the inverse Fourier transform of the dynamic flexibility matrix.

## Inertia Force

The force that is equal to the mass times the acceleration.

## Inertance

The ratio of the steady state acceleration response to the value of the forcing function for a sinusoidal excitation.

## Kinematically Equivalent Mass

If the mass and stiffness are defined by the same displacement assumptions then a kinematically equivalent mass matrix is produced. This is not a diagonal (lumped) mass matrix.

## Kinetic Energy

The energy stored in the system arising from its velocity. In some cases it can also be a function of the structural displacements.

## Linear System

When the coefficients of stiffness, mass and damping are all constant then the system is linear. Superposition can be used to solve the response equation.

## Lumped Mass Model

The system mass is represented by a number of point masses or particles. The mass matrix is diagonal.

## Multi Degree of Freedom

The system is defined by more than one inertia force.

**Mass**

The constant(s) of proportionality relating the acceleration(s) to the force(s). For a discrete parameter multi degree of freedom model this is usually given as a mass matrix.

**Multi-point Constraint**

Where the constraint is defined by a relationship between more than one displacement at different node points.

**Mobility**

The ratio of the steady state velocity response to the value of the forcing function for a sinusoidal excitation.

**Mode Shape**

Same as the eigenvector.

**Modal Stiffness**

The stiffness associated with the generalised displacements defined by the eigenvectors. Its value has no physical significance since the eigenvector contains an arbitrary normalising factor but the ratio of modal stiffness to modal mass is always the eigenvalue.

**Modal Mass**

The mass associated with the generalised displacements defined by the eigenvectors. Its value has no physical significance since the eigenvector contains an arbitrary normalising factor but the ratio of modal stiffness to modal mass is always the eigenvalue.

**Modal Damping**

The damping associated with the generalised displacements defined by the eigenvectors. Its value has no physical significance since the eigenvector contains an arbitrary normalising factor.

## Natural Mode

Same as the eigenvector.

## Non-Holonomic Constraints

Constraints that can only be defined at the level of infinitesimal displacements. They cannot be integrated to give global constraints.

## Non-Linear System

When at least one of the coefficients of stiffness, mass or damping vary with displacement or time then the system is non-linear. Superposition cannot be used to solve the problem.

## Non-Stationary Random

A force or response that is random and its statistical properties vary with time.

## Over Damped System

A system which has an equation of motion where the damping is greater than critical. It has an exponentially decaying, non-oscillatory impulse response.

## Participation Factor

The fraction of the mass that is active for a given mode with a given distribution of dynamic loads. Often this is only defined for the specific load case of inertia (seismic) loads.

## Periodic Response (Force)

A response (force) that regularly repeats itself exactly.

## Phase Angle

The ratio of the in phase component of a signal to its out of phase component gives the tangent of the phase angle of the signal relative to some reference.

## Proportional Damping

A damping matrix that is a linear combination of the mass and stiffness matrices. The eigenvectors of a proportionally damped system are identical to those of the undamped system.

## Random Analysis

The applied loading is only known in terms of its statistical properties. The loading is non-deterministic in that its value is not known exactly at any time but its mean, mean square, variance and other statistical quantities are known.

## Receptance

The ratio of the steady state displacement response to the value of the forcing function for a sinusoidal excitation. It is the same as the dynamic flexibility.

## Rigid Body Displacement

A non-zero displacement pattern that has zero strain energy associate with it.

## Single Degree of Freedom

The system is defined by a single inertia force.

## Single Point Constraint

Where the constraint is unique to a single node point.

## Stationary Random

A force or response that is random but its statistical characteristics do not vary with time.

## Steady State Response

The response of the system to a periodic forcing function when all of the transient components of the response have become insignificant.

## Stiffness

The parameter(s) that relate the displacement(s) to the force(s). For a discrete parameter multi degree of freedom model this is usually given as a stiffness matrix.

## Strain Energy

The energy stored in the system by the stiffness when it is displaced from its equilibrium position.

## Superposition

For a linear system the response is the same if it is found by adding together two or more separate forcing functions and then solving the equations or by solving for the separate forcing functions and then adding the responses together. The second method of solving for each forcing function and adding the response is superposition. A modal solution and a Fourier series solution both imply superposition.

## Time Domain

The structures forcing function and the consequent response is defined in terms of time histories. The Fourier transform of the time domain gives the corresponding quantity in the frequency domain.

## Transient Response

The component of the system response that does not repeat itself regularly with time.

## Undamped Natural Frequency

The square root of the ratio of the stiffness to the mass (the square root of the eigenvalue). It is the frequency at which an undamped system vibrates naturally. A system with n degrees of freedom has n natural frequencies.

## Under Damped System

A system which has an equation of motion where the damping is less than critical. It has an oscillatory impulse response.

## Velocity

The first time derivative of the displacement.

## Virtual Displacement

An arbitrary imaginary change of the system configuration consistent with its constraints.

### Viscous Damping

The damping is viscous when the damping force is proportional to the velocity.

# BIBLIOGRAPHY

1. W.C. Hurty and M.F. Rubinstein, *Dynamics of Structures*, Prentice-Hall, 1964
2. R.W. Clough and J Penzien, *Dynamics of Structures*, McGraw-Hill, 1975
3. S. Timoshenko, D.H. Young and W. Weaver Jr,. *Vibration Problems in Engineering*, 4thEd., John Wiley & Sons, 1974
4. K.-J. Bathe and E.L. Wilson, *Numerical Methods in Finite Element Analysis*, Prentice-Hall, 1976
5. J.S. Przemieniecki, *Theory of Matrix Structural Analysis*, McGraw-Hill, 1968
6. C.M. Harris and C.E. Crede, *Shock and Vibration Handbook*, 2nd Ed., McGraw-Hill, 1976
7. L. Meirovitch, *Analytical Methods in Vibration*, MacMillan, 1967
8. L. Meirovitch, *Elements of Vibration Analysis*, McGraw-Hill, 1975
9. M. Paz, *Structural Dynamics Theory and Computation*, Van Nostrand, 1980
10. W.T. Thompson, *Theory of Vibrations with Applications*, Prentice-Hall, 1981
11. R.R. Craig, *Structural Dynamics, An Introduction to Computer Methods*, John Wiley & Sons, 1981
12. S.H. Crandall and W.D. Mark, *Random Vibration in Mechanical Systems*, Academic Press, 1963
13. D.J. Ewins, *Modal Testing: Theory and Practice*, Research Studies Press, 1984
14. Bendat and Piersol, *Random Data: Analysis and Measurement Procedures*, Wiley-Interscience, 1971
15. T.J.R. Hughes, *The Finite Element Method. Linear Static and Dynamic Finite Element Analysis*, Prentice Hall, 1987
16. K.J. Bathe, *Finite Element Procedures in Engineering Analysis*, Prentice Hall, 1982
17. A.R. Collar and A. Simpson, *Matrices and Engineering Dynamics*, Ellis Horwood, 1987
18. R.A. Frazer, W.J. Duncan and A. Collar, *Elementary Matrices*, AMS Press Inc., 1983

20.  P. Lancaster, *Lambda Matrices and Vibrating Systems*, Pergamon Press, 1966

21.  J.H. Wilkinson, *The Algebraic Eigenvalue Problem*, Oxford University Press, 1965

22.  J.W.S. Rayleigh, *The Theory of Sound*, Dover Publications, 1945

23.  R.E.D. Bishop and D.C. Johnson *The Mechanics of Vibration*, Cambridge University Press, 1960

24.  A. Jennings, *Matrix Computation for Engineers and Scientists*, John Wiley & Sons, 1977

25.  M. Petyt, *Introduction to Finite Element Vibration Analysis*, Cambridge University Press, 1990

# INDEX